LIFE NATURE LIBRARY

ANIMAL BEHAVIOUR

LIFE NATURE LIBRARY

ANIMAL BEHAVIOUR

by Niko Tinbergen

and The Editors of TIME-LIFE BOOKS

TIME
LIFE
BOOKS

TIME-LIFE INTERNATIONAL (NEDERLAND) B.V.

About the Author

Niko Tinbergen's interest in animals began to manifest itself when, as 'a boy in the Netherlands, he kept sticklebacks in an aquarium. As he watched hour after hour the activities of these fascinating little fish, he was forming, without knowing it, a lifelong habit of close observation of animals in their natural surroundings, which would eventually lead him to international eminence in the field of ethology, or animal behaviour. Educated in the Netherlands, he received his doctorate at the University of Leyden and later became associated with the leading behavioural pioneer, Konrad Lorenz. In England he organized a department of research in animal behaviour at Oxford University. As professor of animal behaviour there, he has not only continued his behavioural studies but has also trained numerous young research workers and has still found time to travel widely, co-ordinating the efforts of behavioural scientists in other countries. He is perhaps best known for research into the behaviour of sea birds, and he has spent many years studying the habits of gulls in Europe, America, Africa and the Arctic. Some of the insights gained in these studies appeared in *The Herring Gull's World*. His other books include *The Study of Instinct*, *Bird Life*, *Social Behaviour in Animals* and *Curious Naturalists*. Two books for children, *Kleew* and *The Tale of John Stickle*, were originally written in letters to his children during two years of internment in a World War II German prison camp. Dr. Tinbergen was elected a Fellow of the Royal Society in 1962.

ON THE COVER: A honey-bee presents a load of pollen to the hive for inspection. Next it will perform its celebrated pollen dance—an intricate series of movements that will explain to the other bees where to find pollen themselves.

Contents

Introduction

THE study of animal behaviour began with early man's first systematic attempts to draw conclusions and make predictions from his observations of the creatures around him. Yet today it remains as one of the most complex and challenging branches of all science. In fact, at present we seem closer to understanding the origins of life itself than we are to understanding how and why most living things behave as they do.

The complexity of animal behaviour study does not depend on elaborate mathematical treatments, on delicate instruments or giant computers—the paraphernalia that people usually associate with science. Although these devices have their place, they are after all only a means of wringing facts from nature, and an experienced student of animal behaviour armed with binoculars and hidden in a blind can gather in a few hours enough facts about his subject to keep him pondering for a year. The challenge is mainly to the intellect, to the judgement and patience of the observer rather than to his technical ingenuity.

This would seem to place animal behaviour study pretty far from particle physics, but both fields are, in truth, plagued by the same problem: what would the animal (or particle) be doing if the observer were not present as a slight disturber of its environment? Attempts to resolve this problem range all the way from laboratory experiments, conducted under the most rigidly controlled conditions, to field observations in which the student makes elaborate efforts to conceal himself so that the animal will be left as undisturbed as possible to go about its business amidst the many natural variables of its environment. Neither approach is sufficient by itself; both are necessary.

The emphasis that the behaviourist places on keeping an animal's surroundings undisturbed springs from his conviction that its behaviour is meaningful only in the sense that it has enabled the species to survive and evolve to its present status under prevailing environmental conditions. A tiger's teeth and a fish's fins have evolutionary significance not only in their shape but also in how and where they are used. Modern students of animal behaviour, among whom Dr. Tinbergen is a leader, have repeatedly shown that relatedness of different animal species is just as surely expressed by comparing their behaviour patterns as by comparing their body forms.

Being comparative, behaviour study is not a field for the narrow specialist. Dr. Tinbergen's distinguished work includes analysis of the homing of wasps, the courtship of butterflies and the nesting behaviour of sea birds. His wide experience and deep insights are here combined in a fascinating volume which constitutes not only a challenge but an encouragement to every reader. Anyone, Dr. Tinbergen seems to say, with a sharp eye and ear, a measure of patience and a healthy scepticism about jumping to conclusions, can profitably study animals and may conceivably make observations of lasting value to science.

KENNETH D. ROEDER
Professor of Physiology
Department of Biology
Tufts University

1

An Infant Science

THE vast majority of people, wherever they live and whatever their occupa-
tion, come in contact with animals in one way or another and have to deal
with them. It is obvious that the hunter has to know the ways of his quarry;
that the farmer must be aware of the habits of his farmyard animals and of
creatures that damage his crops; that the fisherman must know when and where
to find his fish and how to outwit them. Even the modern city dweller meets
animals: he may want to ward off the cockroaches in his kitchen or he may keep
a dog or bird and grow familiar with the way his pet behaves. All over the
world, among primitive tribes as well as in modern society, there are those
who delight in the observation of animals, and there is a growing awareness
of the fact that sharing our world with our fellow creatures is like travelling
together—we enjoy being surrounded by other beings who, like ourselves, are
deeply absorbed in the adventure of living. There is a growing sense of marvel,
and also of affinity.

But man experiences much more than just this sense of awareness of other
forms of life; he tends to do more than just look at animals. It is one of his
special attributes that man *wonders* about the world he lives in. He wants to

CHARLES DARWIN, 1809-1882

Before Darwin treated behaviour, along with structure, as an important part of an animal's equipment for survival, most natural scientists judged animal behaviour by human standards, or ignored it altogether. But Darwin's work on animal and human behaviour, far in advance of his time, paved the way for scientific, objective experiments and observations.

J. HENRI FABRE, 1823-1915

Fabre's importance lies in his having been the first to make detailed observations of animals in their natural surroundings and the first to keep minute and orderly records of what he saw. He spent 40 years watching the bees and wasps in his garden in France, and astonished the world with evidence of how complex the behaviour of insects really is.

see exactly how things happen, and he wants to understand why they happen.

This sense of wonder is at the root of scientific inquiry, and so it was inevitable that the desire to understand the behaviour of animals should lead to the study of animal behaviour. This inquiry—which is still in its infancy—is concerned with far more than just recording interesting incidents of animal life. It tries to find out as exactly as possible "what makes animals tick": why animals behave the way they do. I have spent the greater part of my life at this task, associating with animals in the field and in the laboratory, observing them and studying their responses in a variety of experimental situations. I have, in 30 years or so, seen our understanding of animal behaviour grow considerably. But I know only too well that our science has still a very long way to go. I am only one single member of a guild in which thousands of psychologists, zoologists, physiologists, ecologists and geneticists are jointly building a new science. Most of the questions we ask are still unanswered. Worse, we are not always sure that we are asking the right questions or applying the right methods. We are hardly more than groping to find our way. But these early stages of scientific exploration are fascinating; they give one a sense of adventure, and I firmly believe that many of my fellow men are willing and indeed keen to join me in this adventure. I therefore intend in this book to depart somewhat from the practice of previous volumes in the LIFE Nature Library—while I hope to be informative, I have laid emphasis on the lines of thought, on the methods of approach applied by biologists in their attempts to understand animal behaviour rather than on the factual information which, over the years, builds up a body of scientific knowledge.

WHERE do we begin? At the beginning—by asking ourselves: What exactly *is* animal behaviour? What do we mean by it? The answer cannot be straightforward and simple. Roughly speaking, behaviour is the movements animals make. These involve more than running, swimming, crawling and other types of locomotion. They also comprise the movements animals make when feeding, when mating, even when breathing. Nor is this all: slight movements of parts of the body, such as pricking the ears or making a sound, are also parts of behaviour. And many animals do something akin to our blushing—they change colour, sometimes as a way of concealing themselves from predators, on other occasions when they are aroused to attack or are courting a female. It is difficult to distinguish this sharply from behaviour. And, of course, behaviour can also consist of standing still and looking intently or, perhaps, just thinking—doing something internally that may influence subsequent behaviour.

On the whole, however, we tend to call "behaviour" movement or a change of movement, including the change from motion to absolute non-motion, or "freezing"—in short, what one can directly observe. But even though we may start by studying these observable things, as we observe more closely, and particularly as we apply more analytical methods, we are able to see more and more of the processes that go on inside the animal, and behaviour itself becomes an increasingly vague concept as attention focuses increasingly on the machinery behind it. However, for practical purposes, saying that we are concerned with movements will do.

Animals behave in a bewildering variety of ways; in fact, the range of animal behaviour patterns is as great as that of their many shapes, sizes and colours, which took generations of zoologists to describe and classify. No two species behave exactly alike. A robin can be recognized by its song and also by the way it feeds on one's lawn, by the nest it builds and by its threat and court-ship postures. And there can be surprisingly many different types of behaviour in one and the same species of animal too. Gulls may feed by plunge-diving for fish or by killing a sick bird or by foot-paddling to drive worms to the surface of a meadow, or even by hawking insects on the wing. Yet the behaviour repertoire of such species is limited—no gull catches a bird the way a falcon does, nor can a robin build an oven-bird's nest. The enormous variety of behaviour repertoires has as yet been described only very sketchily, and the behaviour of most animals is very imperfectly known. But enough is already known to set us wondering about what it all means, to ask questions about behaviour; and this natural progression from description to inquiry leads us deeper and deeper into the subject.

THE next question generally asked by the student of behaviour is: Why does an animal behave the *way* it does? This seems simple and straightforward enough, but it is really two questions in one—and as we shall see, both are important to the biologist.

Let us say we are watching a dog eat. When we ask ourselves, Why is it eating? we may mean, To what purpose, to what end does it eat; what is the use of eating? One answer, of course, is that it eats in order to survive, or, to put it more specifically, the effect of eating contributes to the dog's survival. This is one aspect of behaviour—and an important one—which we shall deal with later: much of behaviour has survival value. This is of course obvious with eating, but the way other behaviours contribute to survival is not at all obvious and has to be investigated in detail.

However, there is the second question implicit in the one we are pursuing: when we ask why a dog eats, we may also be asking, What makes it eat? In this case we are not inquiring about the effects of its behaviour but about its causes. Now it becomes relevant to know whether or not the dog has been starved, whether it is stimulated by the sight and smell of food, and whether, when it was young, it learnt where and when to seek food.

The study of the survival value of behaviour is now in an extremely interesting phase. Just over a century ago Charles Darwin shook the world with his theory of evolution through natural selection, in which he proposed that the wonderful adaptability of all animals and plants was not due to sudden creation but to a long process of evolution. The present organisms, he said, had through the aeons become what they were through continuous selection of the fittest individuals, allowing these to outbreed the less well-adapted variants. Obviously this theory made it necessary to find out whether the peculiarities of each species really contributed to fitness, particularly those properties which seemed at first glance just "odd" and "improbable". Thus attention focused on the discovery and description of extreme examples of adaptive structures and behaviours. Many fascinating discoveries were made in this post-Darwinian period; one of the most famous is the case of the yucca moth.

The female of the yucca moth is one of the few moths equipped with an ovipositor through which she lays her eggs. This tiny tube is needle-sharp because the moth must thrust it through the wall of the ovary in the yucca flower to lay her eggs inside. Invariably, when she has done this, she collects yucca pollen and pollinates the stigma, an act which ensures that her larvae will have a plentiful supply of seeds to feed on when they develop. Since there are many more seeds than the larvae will consume, the plant is not harmed, and this

C. LLOYD MORGAN, 1852-1936

Although Lloyd Morgan reached his prime 50 years after Darwin, scientists were still trying to interpret animal behaviour in terms of human acts and feelings. Lloyd Morgan helped to put an end to that for ever by showing that one can often find a simpler mental process to explain the act of an animal, and that the simplest explanation may be the right one.

IVAN PAVLOV, 1849-1936

Pavlov's career was centred on the laboratory and the controlled experiment. In a classic test series, he made a dog's mouth water by always giving an artificial stimulus, such as ringing a bell, at feeding time. Soon, he found, the dog's mouth watered in anticipation of food whenever the bell rang. Thus was born the key concept of the conditioned reflex.

11

symbiotic interplay ensures the survival of both plant and insect—without each other, both species would die out.

Surprising as this intricate relationship is, the yucca moth is a true example of insect behaviour—but it also illustrates the trap into which this fascinating and important study fell in the post-Darwinian era. Some men went so far in supporting improbable theories about the survival value of organs, colour patterns and behaviour that they gradually discredited this whole line of research. One well-known and respected naturalist seriously claimed that the bright-pink coloration of the roseate spoon-bill served to camouflage this bird at sunrise and sunset—without trying to consider how the bird managed the rest of the time. It was many years before a more balanced approach and more sophisticated, partly experimental methods at last began to win new adherents to the field— but the new thinking is now paying off handsomely in terms of discoveries that lead us ever deeper into the subject.

There is, for instance, a small fish called the stickleback which habitually builds a tubular nest in the water and, after inducing one or more females to spawn in it, guards it with an intriguing behavioural pattern. It alternates periods of just swimming around the nest with periods of what looks remarkably as though it were fanning it: the fish dips head down, facing the nest, and for as long as 30 seconds appears to direct water at it by moving its fins in a quick, regular rhythm, making forward swimming motions the while with its tail so as to stay in position.

Why does the stickleback do this? A few simple experiments yield an almost absurdly simple answer: it *is* fanning the nest; it is ventilating the eggs, keeping them supplied with freshly aerated water. If the male is removed, the eggs will die. They also die if the male is allowed to stay and fan but if the nest is shielded with a watch glass. They do not die if the male is removed and replaced by a glass tube through which water is regularly directed at the nest. But it must be freshly aerated water and it must be aimed at the nest; if the tube does not provide water or if stale water is pumped through it, the eggs will not survive.

Probing into the functional significance of behaviour patterns is like a journey of exploration and discovery; at every step one is faced with surprises. The problem can be approached in two ways. First, one may observe a certain behaviour, as we did with the stickleback's fanning, and ask, What would be the use of this? But one can also look at an aspect of animal life, a pressure of the environment, let us say, like that of being preyed upon; in this case one may ask how the animal deals with this pressure.

Usually, of course, both approaches are applied together. The student begins his research by simply observing, and on the basis of his observations he tries to formulate a hunch as to the most likely purpose of the behaviour he sees. We first conceived the idea that fanning of sticklebacks might ventilate the eggs when we saw that the male's fin movements directed a water jet at the nest entrance. Knowing that growing eggs require oxygen, we put two and two together and promoted our hunch to a hypothesis, which was then tested with a few experiments.

Then, however, we applied the second approach and asked whether just fanning was all that was required. Sure enough, we found that, as the eggs grew and required more oxygen, the amount of fanning increased. We also learned that half-way through the period of parental care the male begins to construct a number of extra openings in the roof of the nest to make ventilation more efficient, and we saw the significance of the male's exact orientation during fanning, which ensured that the water jet he sent down actually entered the nest.

Black-headed gulls, which nest in large colonies in dunes on the sea beaches, like many other birds take away the empty egg shell each time a chick has hatched. Why do they do this? By considering various possibilities, we thought it most likely that this was useful in concealment, since a piece of shell with its conspicuous white inside lying right next to the chick might serve as a signal to a predator that there was a meal nearby. So we decided to test this hypothesis, and we began our tests with crows, since these birds are the chief predators of young black-headed gulls. We discovered that nests that had pieces of shell lying within eight inches of them were investigated and attacked by crows far more often than those that had no shells. With this significant piece of knowledge, our hypothesis began to have some substance, and we went on to investigate what other defences the gulls had against predators. This led to some fascinating discoveries. For example, we learned that there was a reason for the gulls' habit of all laying their eggs at about the same time. This proved to have a direct bearing on brood survival; birds laying a little before the others, and birds laying a little after, lost their broods much more often to predators.

THE habit of nesting in dense colonies also reduced predation, for when we laid out extra eggs in lines running from well inside to well outside the colony, we found that the outside eggs were taken much more often than inside eggs, which were protected because the gulls attacked in force and repelled any predator trying to steal them. We also found, by systematic and prolonged studies, that the gulls' habit of spending nights in non-nesting periods on broad, open beaches was a very effective, if indirect, defence against foxes. Although foxes roamed over the beach as well as over the dunes, they killed many more gulls in the dunes, where they had a better chance to come up on them unawares, than on the beach. Only on exceptionally dark nights did they have much luck in getting at the gulls on the beach.

Thus, by systematic observation and, where possible, by devising an experiment to test whether or not a certain behaviour characteristic contributes to success, the student gradually becomes aware of the intricate adaptability of animal behaviour. He begins to see more and more clearly that behaviour is an essential part of an animal's equipment for survival. Even though we have so far done no more than scratch the surface, a wonderful picture slowly emerges.

First of all, the movements themselves are often incredibly efficient. The cuttle-fish, an inshore squid, can circumvent the defences of shrimps in a very interesting way. As it swims leisurely a few inches above the sandy bottom, it spouts a gentle jet of water at regular intervals through its funnel, aiming down and a little ahead. Every time it does so, the sand in front is whirled up. The function of this becomes clear when one sees the water jet hit a buried shrimp. These shrimps are wonderfully camouflaged, and they conceal themselves even better by lying under a thin layer of sand, which they sweep over their backs with a wide, backward movement of their two antennae. When a cuttle-fish happens to expose a shrimp by whirling up its protective blanket of sand, the shrimp quickly covers itself again. This is its undoing, for the cuttle-fish, which might have overlooked the shrimp had it remained still, detects the movement. It immediately shoots out two tentacles and seizes the shrimp with the sucking discs at their tips.

Not only are the movements themselves nicely adapted to their functions but also their timing, their orientation and their co-ordination with other movements. It is notable that the cuttle-fish does his "sand puffing" only when he is hunting shrimps; to be successful he must aim his water jet at the sand bottom ahead of him; he must at the same time swim in a very special, leisurely way; and he must be ready to strike when he sees a shrimp move. It may seem commonplace, but when you think of it, it is really wonderful that he *does* all this. So if we want to understand how behaviour contributes to success we also have to find out how efficient it is or, looking at it from the other side, what would go wrong if the animal behaved differently, and why the behaviour would misfire. This, however, must await a later chapter.

**HOW A CUTTLE-FISH
SNARES A SHRIMP**

Efficient co-ordination of two separate acts in order to get food, even among fairly primitive organisms, is nowhere better demonstrated than by the cuttlefish. One of its foods is shrimps that lie concealed in the sand on the ocean bottom. As it swims along, the cuttle-fish gently blows away the sand with a jet of water and occasionally uncovers a shrimp (above). If the shrimp were to lie still, it would be passed by unnoticed, but it hastily covers itself up again, and this movement alerts the cuttle-fish, which snatches it up in its tentacles (below).

THE quest for the causes underlying behaviour leads to equally fascinating research, though of quite a different kind. We have, of course, known for a long time that, mechanically speaking, behaviour is a consequence of muscle activity, and that muscles on the whole do not contract unless stimulated by nerves. The way muscles work and the way nerves make them contract are the proper study of the physiologist, and a great deal is already known. But rarely is behaviour a matter of an isolated contraction of one muscle. On the contrary, even the simpler behaviour patterns, such as locomotion, are sequences of contractions and relaxations of very many muscles, all well modulated and well timed. In fact, behaviour is almost always a symphony of muscle contractions, with the messages from the central nervous system organized in an orderly manner, and it is this organization we have to understand.

The central nervous system, for its part, does not act entirely on its own accord—it receives stimulation from other sources. What are these sources? Partly they are the sense organs—eyes, ears, nose and many others—which provide the animal with information about the outside world. The sensory processes, therefore, must also enter into our study. But partly, too, behaviour is controlled from within: a hungry animal sets out to feed, and when its sex urge awakens it goes out in search of a mate. We shall have to find out what it is inside the animal that makes it hungry or stimulates its sex urge. And finally, there is the fact that outside stimuli and internal condition interact—i.e., a hungry animal reacts to the food stimuli while a satiated animal does not; outside the mating season, as in winter, most animals are indifferent to the same sex partners that strongly attracted them in the mating season.

There are two major difficulties in this study of the causes of animal behaviour, and unless they are clearly recognized, they can hamper research seriously. The first concerns the subjective experiences of an animal: does it feel anything akin to what we feel when we are, say, angry or sad or amused? The biologist simply does not know and cannot know, and for that reason he does not feel he is entitled to say anything on the subject. Therefore, pursuing a strict and scientifically consistent line of inquiry, he cannot say that an animal attacks "because it is angry" or that it retreats "because it is afraid". He has to express the cause of what we might interpret as anger in terms of processes that can, in principle, be observed and measured just as well as the behaviour itself. In short, he is interested in the machinery of behaviour.

A second possible source of confusion is our failure to distinguish the two meanings of "why". We are apt to say, for instance, that an animal eats *because* it needs food, that a bird builds a nest *because* it requires a receptacle for its eggs. Again, we have to go beyond the superficial meaning of the word, and in order to avoid ambiguity biologists are strict about its use. In their language, "because" refers literally to causes, to events which precede the behaviour and which can be shown to control it.

The confusion arises because we ourselves can, in some way still mysterious to the scientist, think ahead: even before we decide whether or not we shall undertake a particular form of behaviour, we can imagine what the effect of that behaviour will be. Thus we can say, with a certain justification, that the *effect* of our behaviour controls what we shall do before we have done it. But although many animals do things—such as building a nest, feeding their young, hoarding food—that prove to be useful long after they do it, they do not really seem to have these distant aims "in mind" when they are doing them. Certainly they often show surprisingly little adjustment to abnormal conditions that may arise; in such circumstances their behaviour frequently "misfires". If a young song-bird is accidentally kicked out of the nest and gets chilled, it fails to open its mouth for food when a parent comes and so is neither fed nor brooded—it perishes, simply because the parents cannot cope with this unexpected development; they brood only young that are in the nest and feed only young that gape. What they react to, much more rigidly than we, is the stimuli of the moment. And while it is true to say that the *function* of feeding the young is to make them grow up—a distant aim—the *causes* of feeding the young are found in stimuli, external and internal, without which this end would not be reached. We would find out little about such causes if we would content ourselves with assuming that animals, like human beings, plan their behaviour with distant aims in mind.

THE search for causes is really endless. Because every cause has in its turn a cause, we are led to probe continuously further back in time. In doing so, we find that the life of an animal runs in cycles; behaviour often repeats itself. Periods of feeding alternate with intervals in which the animal, satiated at first, gradually becomes hungry again. Other cycles are on a larger time scale; sexual behaviour in many animals comes only once a year. But when one looks back still further, one comes ultimately to a stage in the life of the animal when it was still growing up, when it was still developing. During development an animal's behaviour changes just as its form does, and the causal organization of this behavioural development determines how the adult shall behave. In order to understand what makes an animal behave the way it does, we must, therefore, do more than study the immediate causes of the self-repeating cycles of behaviour: we must also ask how this fully geared, cycling machinery has become what it is. Although, in practice, research on the behaviour machinery of the full-grown animal necessarily overlaps with studies of its development—for animals, like man, keep developing through adult life—it will be practical to deal with these two fields of research one by one, and behaviour development will not be discussed until Chapter 6.

But the life of one animal is itself a cycle in a series of events that happens on a much larger time scale. Generation follows generation, and through countless generations the animals we know today evolved until they became something else and behaved differently. This, too, concerns us: we have to ask how animals and their behaviour have changed through evolution, how they have become different from each other, and how they have become increasingly efficient. This task differs fundamentally from other kinds of biological study. We can observe the behaviour, and its development, directly in present-day animals, and can repeat these observations, as well as our experiments, as often as we like. But the behaviour of animals of the past can no longer be seen; we are in the position of historians who have no documents of past events. Nevertheless, as we shall see, there are indirect ways of unravelling the biological past. Also, we can study the evolution which animals are undergoing even now and, on the assumption that the laws of evolution have not changed, apply our findings to what went before.

The study of the causes of behaviour, therefore, embraces three relatively distinct tasks: we need to understand how the behaviour machinery works, how it develops during the life of the individual, and how animals have evolved their behaviour machinery through the generations. All these tasks are now being taken in hand. Yet although thousands of trained researchers are spending all their energy and time on this work and are making good progress, they are constantly discovering how much there is they do not know. The emphasis on the need to confine ourselves to what we can actually observe has, so to speak, boomeranged: we discover that there is so amazingly much to observe. Straightforward observation and description in ever-increasing detail is therefore an important part of our task.

FORTUNATELY we need no longer rely on what we can immediately see and hear; we have now at our disposal the still and cine cameras, with time lapse and slow motion, and sounds can not only be heard but also recorded on tape to be heard again and again, and even analysed in the sound spectrograph. Many refined precision techniques are used in experiment. Tiny quantities of hormones can be assessed; electrodes only a few thousandths of a millimetre in diameter can probe into the nervous systems of living animals; data too numerous to handle are fed into computers which, by doing our sums for us quickly and reliably, free us to get on with our real work: observation and experiment.

The complexity of the research and the variety of phenomena are leading to a high degree of specialization among research workers. Animal behaviour is being studied by people of highly varied interests and abilities. Some study the functioning of parts of the total machinery, such as sense organs or even one particular sense organ, others focus on nerve cells or muscles. Still others disentangle the complicated processes occurring during the development of behaviour. Others again study the way behaviour has changed during evolution. Some prefer to work under controlled conditions in the laboratory, others study animals in their natural environment, and there are those who work in zoos. There are specialists on animal groups or even on single animal species, and there are specialists who compare as many species as they can. In spite of this necessary division of labour, there is among behaviour students of all kinds a growing sense of a common aim, and psychologists and zoologists and physiologists are beginning to join forces in a common effort.

We are still very far from completely understanding the behaviour of animals, but we are beginning to learn how we can arrive at such an understanding. We also feel that our task is urgent. Some animals, such as those we consider pests, are a direct threat to us, to our health and our food supplies; we must know how to keep them in check. Others, such as our cattle and consumable fish, are indispensable to us; they have to be farmed, bred and cropped sensibly. We also have to learn to live and let live—to share our planet with our fellow creatures, and this task of conservation, too, requires understanding. And, finally, since we are really related to our fellow animals, a closer study of their behaviour can help us in learning to understand ourselves.

LOVING SNOW GEESE BRACKET THE SHAGGY HEAD OF KONRAD Z. LORENZ, WHO HAS TRAINED THEM TO THINK OF HIM AS THEIR MOTHER

Into the Animal's World

Because it is still a young and uncharted science, animal behaviour is approached in as many different ways as there are scientists. Unique as these individual methods may be, they all have a common purpose—to probe ever deeper into the mystery of animal life. In the following pages photographer Nina Leen shows the ways in which 10 prominent behavioural scientists pursue their research.

Parent to a Science

In the early years, two distinct schools of thought divided the science of animal behaviour. Europeans, calling themselves "ethologists", concentrated on instinctive behaviour, observing and testing animals in the wild. The American school of "psychologists" was more interested in what it could learn of behaviour under controlled laboratory conditions. But both sides respected one man, the Austrian Konrad Z. Lorenz, whom Julian Huxley has called "the father of modern ethology". A scientist with a love for all living things, Lorenz laid the groundwork for many of the most important lines of research still pursued today. He never looked at animals in terms of people, as many of the behaviourists had always done, but formulated a new school of investigation, based on his conviction that an animal's behaviour, like its physical adaptations, was part of its equipment for survival and the product of adaptive evolution. He proved his point with a wide variety of creatures which he took into his daily life—shrews, frogs, ducks, monkeys, dogs and others, even learning the "language" of some species so that he could approach them on their own level. Among the many basic truths shown by his experiments, all conducted with animals roaming freely in their natural surroundings, were such learning processes as those shown here, where goslings have been successfully taught to accept Lorenz as their "mother".

AS AQUATIC AS HIS YOUNG CHARGES, LORENZ ENCOURAGES HIS GOSLINGS IN THE WATER WITH SOUNDS WHICH EFFECTIVELY IMITATE THEIR OWN

ACTING THE MOTHER, Lorenz carries food for his brood on the grounds of the research institute he directs in Bavaria. His work with goslings revealed much about the development of early instinctive behaviour.

"LANGUAGE". HE HAS DESCRIBED HIMSELF AS A "PEASANT TYPE OF NATURALIST . . . I JUST LIKE TO HAVE ANIMALS, TO OWN THEM . . . TO STUDY THEM"

KARL VON FRISCH TESTS THE COLOUR VISION OF BEES IN THE GARDEN OF HIS AUSTRIAN HOME BY USING YELLOW CARDS TO ATTRACT THEM

The Man Who Found That Bees Could See Colours

A logical approach to fundamental questions over the years made Karl von Frisch a major force in behaviour studies, particularly in the field of animal sense organs. Half a century ago, for example, he challenged the prevalent belief that bees were colour-blind—to believe this, he reasoned, would be to believe that the bright colours of flowers pollinated by bees had no biological significance. By a series of simple experiments with coloured cards, he proved that bees did indeed perceive colours. His further work with a variety of animals, notably many invertebrates and fishes, demonstrated their remarkable sensory capacities, each specifically adapted to the demands of the environment, and often led to conclusions—as in the case of the hearing ability of fishes—that were as fresh as they were revealing.

Student of the Clever Ant

Because he is fascinated by the learning ability of ants, Theodore C. Schneirla has combined years of field work with exhaustive laboratory experiments and has become an expert on their behaviour. He studied army ants in the American tropics, gaining detailed insights into the scent stimuli which largely govern their mass movements. Advancing his research at New York's American Museum of Natural History (*below*), he devised mazes for testing the more common ant species. In the mazes, ants which have negotiated the corridors to the food are quick to find their way again even when denied an odour trail to follow, thus proving that they have the power to memorize the correct path. They are also capable of applying this learning to other mazes, a feat which places them near the peak of insect learning.

A QUICK LEARNER, THE FORMICA ANT CAN TRAVEL THROUGH A TEST MAZE FROM NEST (RIGHT) TO FOOD WITHOUT AN ERROR AFTER 25 TRIES

Prober of an Unheard World

The suspicion long held by scientists that many animals make use of stimuli which are beyond the range of human sense organs was dramatically confirmed in the 1930's by Donald R. Griffin, then a senior at Harvard University. Observing the uncanny ability of bats to navigate in total darkness, Griffin theorized that they might be utilizing their ears rather than their eyes. He took his bats to a laboratory that contained equipment for recording high-frequency sounds, and became one of the first humans to detect the high-pitched squeaks the animals sent out as they flew. These ultrasonic signals bounce off the surface of objects, the reflected sound waves guiding the bats in flight. Since Griffin's discovery of the world of unheard sounds in which bats operate, extensive work has been done not only on the bats' system of echo location but also on similar adaptations in other animals, much of it at the Tropical Research Station of the New York Zoological Society in Trinidad, where these pictures of Griffin were taken.

HUNTING FOR BATS to net and take to the laboratory for study, Griffin and a student assistant, with head lamps lighting the way, emerge from an abandoned mine shaft in Trinidad's dense jungle.

GUIDED BY ECHOES, a fishing bat glides towards a morsel of fish being placed on a wire in a dark testing tank by Griffin. As long as the bait is at the surface, the bat goes right for it, grabbing it with its claws. But when the wire and the bait are lowered beneath the water, the bat has difficulty, since the surface reflects 99.9 per cent of the echo-location signals.

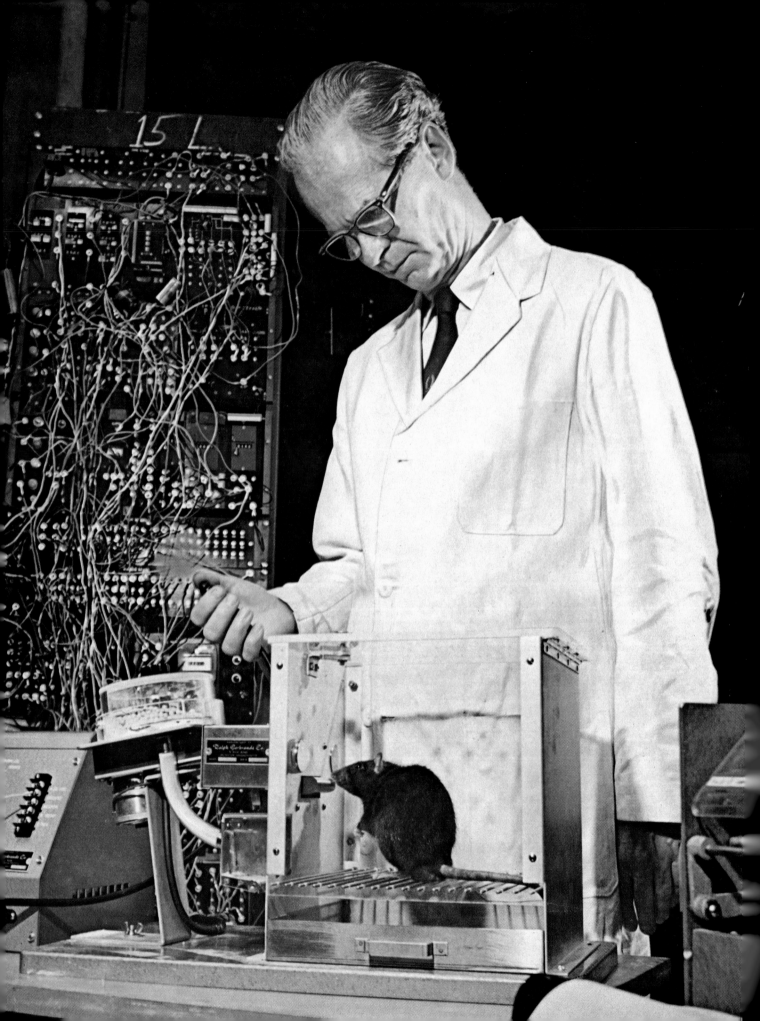

An Apostle of Conditioning

An experimental psychologist at Harvard University, B. Frederic Skinner is famous not only for his mechanized tests on animal behaviour, but also for the fearless, controversial conclusions he draws from them. In his experiments he trains pigeons, rats and other animals to perform a variety of unfamiliar acts by rewarding them immediately—a principle known as "reinforcement". Skinner's test animals are completely insulated from the outside world during the experiments; most often he places them in a closed metal box which has sound-proofed walls and ceiling. His mechanically operated tests have been scheduled with such care and are guided by such modern equipment that the tester may leave the room during the length of the experiment, the results being recorded on an electrically operated graph. Unlike most behaviourists, Skinner has no hesitation in applying to humans what he has seen in the laboratory. Thus, he has elaborated his principle of immediate rewards in devising teaching machines for children which lead them from simple questions through increasingly complex ones by constantly encouraging and approving correct answers. He has also expounded his belief that all behaviour can be artificially controlled, in a Utopian novel, *Walden Two*, where he envisages a land of psychologically conditioned humans living in harmony in an atmosphere free of hate or envy.

A HUNGRY BROWN RAT, with no food in sight, examines a mechanical lever in a Skinner box, here left open for demonstration purposes. The rat in time will learn to press the lever and be rewarded with food, thus "reinforcing" its behaviour.

A BETTER-EDUCATED RAT has been conditioned to push the food lever when a light is on. With the light off (*top*), the rat scratches impatiently; then, as the signal flashes on (*centre*), it lunges at the lever and looks for its reward (*bottom*).

In Quest of Causes

In strong contrast to those behaviourists who study many different animals, Daniel S. Lehrman, director of the Department of Animal Behavior of Rutgers University in New Jersey, has devoted fully 15 years to one species alone—the ring-neck dove. He is hunting for a "system of causes" which would explain, step by step, the complex interaction of the effects of hormones, external stimuli and experience on the development of the dove's behaviour. Thus, for example, Lehrman learned that during the breeding season a female's ovaries and oviducts will enlarge at the mere sight of a male—but less so if the male has been castrated. In countless similar experiments, Lehrman has gone even deeper into behavioural cause and effect; but, he says, "Every good experiment has to raise more questions than it answers"

PROBING THE OVARIES OF A FEMALE DOVE, LEHRMAN DISCLOSES THEIR SWOLLEN STATE, INDUCED BY HORMONAL FLOW AT SIGHT OF A MALE

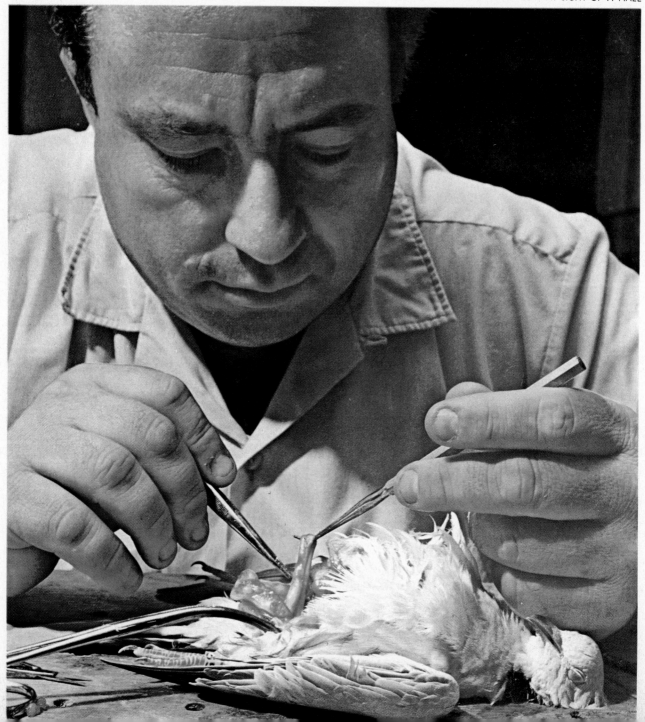

PRESSING WITH A NYLON BRISTLE, HINDE TESTS THE EFFECTS OF HORMONES ON THE SENSITIVITY OF A CANARY'S DEFEATHERED BROOD PATCH

The Complexities of Canaries

Another scientist exploring the complex intermeshing of external and internal factors in the behaviour of animals is Robert A. Hinde of Cambridge University. Working mainly with the common canary, he has charted some of the manifold forces that lead to mating, nest building and egg laying. In the course of his studies, Hinde often alters the chemical balance of his test birds, proving that canary reactions are often dictated by hormones. A female canary, for instance, will begin nest building, a springtime function, at any time of the year if injected with the ovary hormone oestrogen. By documenting scores of similar tests, Hinde has become a world authority on the physiology of reproductive behaviour. A diagram based on his work with canaries appears on pages 94 and 95.

27

An Infant's Vital Needs

Lower animals are not the only ones tested by psychologists in their laboratory experiments. For the past decade, Harry F. Harlow, director of the University of Wisconsin's Primate Laboratory, has been observing the intricate relationship between child and mother as it is manifested in rhesus monkeys. In his tests, each new-born monkey was given access to two artificial "mothers", one a wire frame with wooden face and feeding bottle at breast level, the other roughly the same but with a soft terry cloth covering. The monkeys took milk from both mothers, but as they grew older, they spent more and more time climbing on and clinging to the cloth mother. When faced with an intruder such as a mechanical teddy bear, the monkeys fled to the cloth mother, rubbed against her and then, comforted and unafraid, examined the bear. Similarly, when the monkeys were put in a strange room, they immediately sought out the cloth mother and clung to her for solace before exploring.

Baby monkeys reared without their real mothers or the terry cloth substitutes proved to be incapable of normal relationships with either males or females. As Harlow concluded, the experiments establish the importance of bodily contact in an infant's love and the need for the attention and care of a mother.

CUDDLING UP to a cloth-covered mother, this infant rhesus monkey clearly shows its preference for warmth and comfort, despite the fact that it is the wire dummy that gives it food.

CRINGING IN TERROR, a monkey brought up without a mother or young monkeys to play with shows the effect of abnormal upbringing when a youngster its own age is put in its cage.

EASILY DOMINATED, the same monkey cannot defend itself or engage in play. From these experiments, Harlow learned that contact with other infants was vital to normal development.

29

HARRY HARLOW CRADLES AN INFANT MONKEY IN HIS ARMS AS IT VIEWS ITS WIRE "MOTHER."

PEERING THROUGH A TANK, Eugenie Clark studies a serranoid fish that she captured while scuba diving. This hermaphroditic creature is the subject of many papers by Dr. Clark.

Schoolmistress to Sharks

While most animal behaviourists use such familiar creatures as bats, rats, birds and even monkeys in their research, ichthyologist Eugenie Clark has concerned herself mainly with sharks. Now one of the world's leading specialists in shark physiology, she has proved in her experiments that some shark species can be conditioned, like brown rats in a Skinner box, to learn new behaviour patterns in order to get food. In one series of tests conducted at her Cape Haze Marine Laboratory in Sarasota, Florida, lemon and nurse sharks were trained to press their snouts against a square, white plywood target. This rang an underwater bell and produced a piece of fish as a reward. After a six-week training period, the sharks had learned to swim independently to the target and push it whenever they wanted food. Through such behavioural tests it has been shown that sharks are sensitive to underwater sounds and that they can learn to associate these, as well as visual stimuli, with specific situations such as food getting.

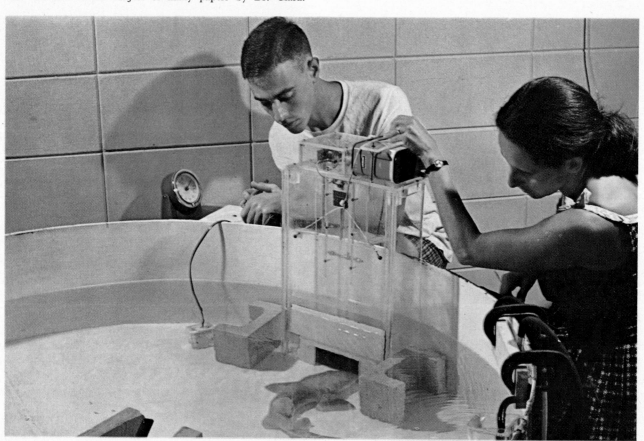

NUDGING THE TARGET, a baby shark, having been alerted by a bell that food is to be had, will be rewarded with a piece of fish. In this advanced test, the bell is the behaviour stimulus.

NURSE (SHARK) EMBRYOS, some of which lived on for a week, are removed by Eugenie Clark. Since pregnant sharks do not feed, they are seldom hooked, and finds like this are rare.

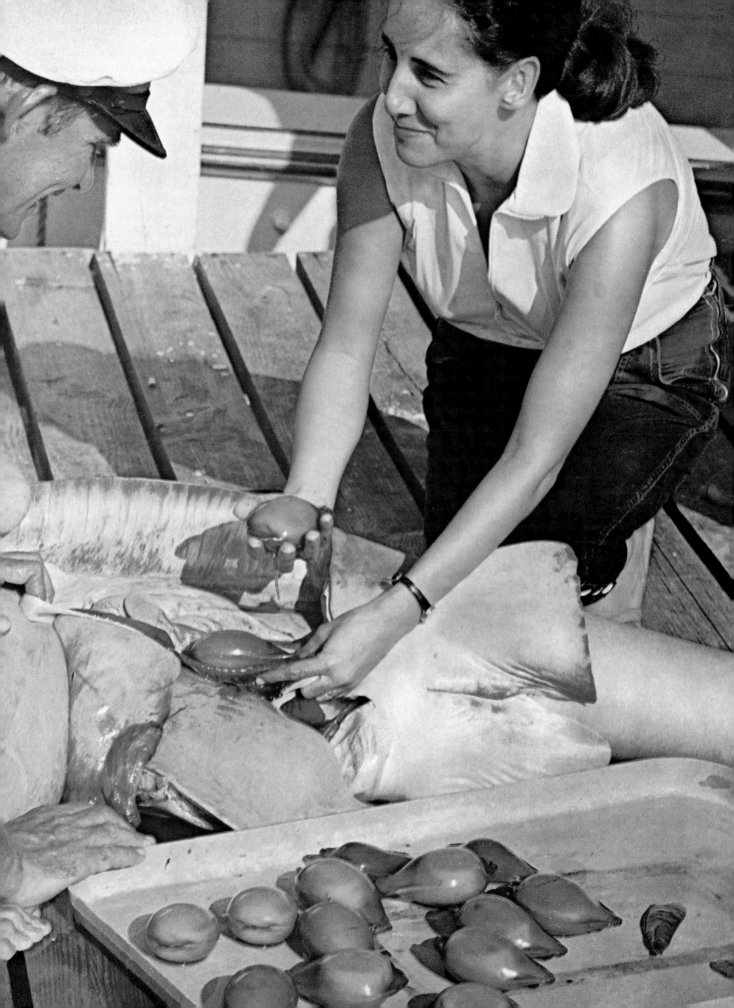

SNIFFING A DEAD TERN, Tinbergen identifies the killer as a fox. Foxes are predators of gulls and, like many other mammals, mark their hunting grounds with strong-smelling urine.

An Observant Naturalist

"I like to study animals in their natural environment. I find that during the long hours of observation in the field, I not only learn about behaviour patterns, but I get ideas, 'hunches', for theories, which I later test by experiments whenever possible. Above all, my ideal is to understand how the complex behaviour machinery of each animal helps it to meet the many pressures of its environment." Thus does Niko Tinbergen, author of this book, sum up his approach to the science of animal behaviour. Through the years he has faithfully followed his own particular code for research and study, wandering in the wilds in search of animals at large.

PAINTING CHICKEN EGGS to resemble those of a gull, Tinbergen prepares a field experiment in camouflage. He showed that painted eggs when scattered were hard for foxes to find.

AMONG THE DUNES of Ravenglass in northern England, Tinbergen strolls, trailed by his pet crow. Always intrigued by nature's changing scenes, he keeps his binoculars at the ready.

2

The Sense Organs: Windows to the World

To be efficient, the behaviour of animals must include the ability to do the right things in the right circumstances. In other words, unless animals carry out the complicated movements we call behaviour at the right moment and in the right place, these will be ineffective. In order to do this, however, they must have information about conditions in the outside world. This information reaches them through their sense organs.

Sensory stimulation is often the starting point of behaviour: a dog sees its master put on his hat and immediately barks in anticipation of a walk, and once outside starts running in pursuit of a scent. Thus he reacts to his environment—and our study of the way behaviour is controlled in animals can therefore logically start with a study of the outside stimuli to which they can respond.

What sort of stimuli do animals receive? First of all, they are not necessarily the same as those to which a human might react. Failure to appreciate this can lead to false conclusions. I once heard of a government official who spent nearly £2,000 on moth-balls to keep birds off the runways of an airport where they collided with jet planes. What he did not know was that birds have a very poorly developed sense of smell—the moth-balls bothered them not at all.

The fact of the matter is that different animals, including man, have different "windows to the world". Some have sensory equipment that in some respects is much poorer than ours; in others, the senses are far superior. There are even animals that react to stimuli which we cannot detect at all—sights or sounds or smells which we could not discover without artificial extensions to our own sense organs. Bees, as we know, see and react to ultra-violet light, whereas we human beings have to transform the ultra-violet rays with special apparatus into the kind of light that we can see.

Once it was realized that animals might have sense organs quite different from our own, it became imperative to explore their sensitivity to outside stimuli systematically and thoroughly. This is a laborious task, but, like all exploration, it is extremely fascinating and rewarding. And the first step in such a study is to find out exactly just what it is in a given situation that an animal is responding to.

KARL VON FRISCH, the famous Austrian zoologist, gave this field of research its initial impetus. His name is rightly connected with his work on bees, but he and his numerous pupils have also done outstanding research on the senses of other animals, particularly on hearing in fishes. One of von Frisch's early papers was simply called "A Fish That Comes When One Whistles"— and indeed he had trained a fish to do just that. However, this was only the beginning; von Frisch also wanted to know *why* the fish came when he whistled, and his line of reasoning illustrates beautifully the research that studies of animals' senses must pursue.

What stimulated the fish to come to the surface when the whistle was blown? Because we can hear, we might assume that the fish could hear too, and that it was responding to the sound. But the fish might not be able to hear—it might have just seen the movements of the man with the whistle and responded to these. How is one to know? One way is to make the same movements, but without whistling. If the fish does not come, clearly it is not movement alone that stimulates it. Conversely, one can whistle without moving and see whether the fish responds. Or one can block off or remove the sense organ that is thought to be responsible for the fish's behaviour, in this case the inner ear: if it fails to come now it may be assumed that it could hear previously. Once it is established that the fish can hear, one can proceed to explore systematically what exactly its hearing organ can achieve—how accurately it can distinguish between different levels of pitch or how weak the sound can be made before the animal fails to react.

Any response which an animal makes naturally—such as coming for food— can be used as an indicator of behaviour. However, these natural responses are not always convenient to work with and not always as clear-cut as an investigator would like. Therefore he may decide to condition or train an animal to a specific stimulus by presenting that stimulus repeatedly together with a natural one. That is what von Frisch was doing when he whistled every time he offered food to the fish. Another way of conditioning is to flash a light every time one feeds an animal, so that it associates light and food. If it can see at all, sooner or later it will respond to the light alone in expectation that food will be present. This training method, as we shall see, is widely used.

Physiologists like to apply still another method of investigation in higher animals: registering the response to a stimulus directly by electrical means. The core of each sense organ is formed by sensory cells, which are the real receivers of the stimulus. Such cells are connected by thin nerve fibres with the central nervous system. These nerve fibres are the communication lines which transmit, in rapid sequence to the brain, volleys of chemo-electrical impulses. These impulses, each lasting a thousandth of a second, register on delicate instruments as "action potentials". Any corresponding variation in their firing pattern indicates that the sense organ is responding to the stimulus. Thus, a light flashed into the eye produces changes in the action potentials in the optic nerve, and these will register on a sensitive meter. However, this method of research also has its limitations, as has the training method. For various reasons the action potentials and behaviour do not invariably tell the same story of sensory capability, so the functions of sense organs are best studied with both methods.

A short review will show the amazing variety of sensory abilities we find among animals. Let us begin by considering the ability to see.

Vision, or responsiveness to light, is one of the five basic senses of the animal kingdom. However, not all animals see the same things. For instance, they are not all sensitive to the same range of the spectrum. We have already noted that bees and many other insects may be sensitive to a wide range of ultra-violet light, but they are far less sensitive to red—in fact, most light that we see as red is invisible to them.

But what about red flowers that are so obviously attractive to insects? Actually, as von Frisch has pointed out, few flowers pollinated by—and therefore adapted to—insects are really red; those that appear red or purple to us reflect a great deal of blue as well, and it is the blue that the insects see. Or consider that popular wild flower, the European poppy. We see it as bright scarlet, but we also observe that it is visited by bees and other insects. A simple test will show that the poppy reflects ultra-violet light which these insects see. We will pick two poppies and flatten them out on a board in a field where poppies grow. One is covered with a filter which absorbs all visible light but admits ultra-violet. The other flower is covered with two filters—one which absorbs all ultra-violet light plus a filter which absorbs all visible light. Both flowers now appear identically black—that is, invisible to our eyes—but the insects will unhesitatingly alight on the first flower, responding to the reflection of the ultra-violet rays.

Many other flowers, such as those of the common cinquefoil, reflect ultra-violet too. These blossoms look uniformly yellow to us, but they reflect a lot of ultra-violet as well. However, each petal has a large patch at its base which does not reflect ultra-violet, and so must appear different—certainly darker—to the bees than the rest of the flower.

ANOTHER interesting question about the vision of animals is whether they actually distinguish colours within the spectrum visible to them or whether they react only to differences in brightness. This can be tested in the same way that human beings are tested for colour vision—with the difference that animals have to be trained in some way to let us know what they see. Again we use the same technique that von Frisch used in getting a fish to respond to a whistle, but this time we introduce colours as stimuli instead of sounds. Suppose, for instance, we train a test animal to associate food with a red triangle by showing it such a triangle every time we offer it food. Once it has learned this, we then show it other triangles that are identical except that they are blue, green, purple—many colours, along with several shades of grey. If the animal still reacts

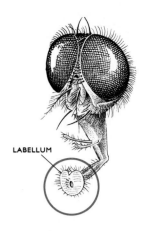

LABELLUM

HOW DO WE KNOW THAT FLIES CAN TASTE?

On the end of the blowfly's proboscis is a spongy pad—the labellum—that is obviously used to help it to identify food, because the fly constantly pokes about with it as if testing the edibility of substances. To prove this, however, required a delicate experiment in which one hair on the labellum was wired to an electric circuit. When this hair was placed in a sugar solution, a minute electrical impulse was produced, showing that tastes do register in the fly's nervous system.

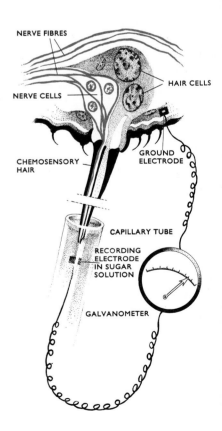

NERVE FIBRES

HAIR CELLS

NERVE CELLS

CHEMOSENSORY HAIR

GROUND ELECTRODE

CAPILLARY TUBE

RECORDING ELECTRODE IN SUGAR SOLUTION

GALVANOMETER

to the red triangle, or to a colour close to red, like purple, can we then assume that it sees colour? Yes, we can—almost. There is a chance that the animal is colour-blind and is "faking" colour vision by recognizing the colour as a certain shade of grey. So we make a test for its ability to discriminate between greys. We train the animal to associate food with only one particular shade of grey, then present it with a whole range of greys of varying shades. If it responds to many greys rather than to the particular one it was trained to, then we can assume that its brightness discrimination is not very accurate, and that its initial response in the colour test was indeed a reaction to colour alone. Of course we must make sure that the animal cannot see either ultra-violet or infra-red light, which some of our test objects might give off.

No animal has yet been discovered that can "see" infra-red light with its eyes, but there are other ways of "seeing" than with eyes alone. Infra-red is a form of heat, and certain creatures, notably the rattlesnake and its relatives, have organs that detect it as effectively as though they "saw" it in our sense of the word. In front of and slightly below their eyes, they have two pits which contain a thin membrane, behind which is a cavity filled with air. The membrane is rich in nerve endings—there are 3,500 in each pit, on a surface of three to four square millimetres, which is about 100,000 times as many as humans have on an equal area of skin. Furthermore, these nerve endings are very close to the surface of the membrane, so that all in all a pit viper, as such snakes are called, can sense from a foot and a half away a tumbler of water only a few degrees warmer than the surrounding air. Rattlesnakes will actually strike at such objects, which makes it seem likely that they use this sensitivity to locate warm-blooded prey. And not only do these organs respond to radiant heat but the fact that they are sunk in pits and have so many nerve endings also enables the snakes to detect the direction from which the heat comes. The rims of the pits act as screens for radiation from the sides; they cast shadows which of course vary with the direction from which the heat reaches the pits. These inform the snakes about the direction of the heat source and enable them to strike with great accuracy.

ANOTHER point of interest in vision is the extent to which an animal can detect details in its visual field. This is by no means a universal accomplishment: many worms and shellfish, for instance, have what is called a "diffuse light sense" in their skins—they see light only the way we feel warmth. All they can really do is to notice whether it is dark or light; they have at best only very poor means of detecting where the light comes from, let alone seeing objects. Higher animals, by contrast, have developed eyes which contain an optical apparatus. Vertebrates use a lens which projects an image on a retina made up of millions of sensory cells, each of which contributes a tiny part to the total visual image. Insects and their relatives have compound eyes—these have no lenses but are made up of a number of conical tubes called ommatidia, which diverge outwards from the optic nerve to give the insect a wide field of vision. Each ommatidium is insulated optically from its neighbours by a mantle of pigment, each provides merely one point of the visual image, and all these points or dots fit together to provide a mosaic-like picture.

Visual acuity, or the ability to distinguish details, is much greater in eyes equipped with lenses than it is in the compound eyes of insects. For a bee, two dots slightly less than one degree of arc apart will merge together indistinguishably into one, but humans, under favourable circumstances, can distinguish between dots only some *40 seconds* of arc apart, or one ninetieth of one degree, and many birds seem to do even better.

Great visual acuity has, of course, many advantages. It allows predatory animals to see their prey from very far away: insect-eating falcons are able to see individual dragon-flies a half a mile distant, whereas for us the same insect becomes indistinguishable at about 100 yards. By the same token, many vulnerable animals can see their predators from afar. Good vision is generally important in many other ways also, of course. We shall see later, for example, that many birds are able to recognize their partners, their flock mates or their young as individuals, and in many cases this is clearly a matter of their recognizing these others of their species by sight.

Probing still deeper into the qualities of vision, we find that much more is involved than mere distinction of quality or quantity of light and discrimination between objects. What, for example, about moving objects? This is an interesting thought: to the element of discernment it adds the element of time. It means that an animal must be able to register differences in the moment of stimulation between cells or groups of cells in the retina. A cine-film is a good illustration of the problem. We know that the pictures we see on the screen do not really move but consist of a series of different still images, each of which falls on a slightly different spot on our retina than its immediate predecessor. The illusion of movement is produced because one element of the retina is able to convey information of the exact moment it was stimulated to other cells that are then stimulated in turn. Thus a constant flow of information and stimulation is set up which in its sum adds up to a picture of movement.

To be able to do this, it is clear that there must be cross-connections between the sensory cells—and indeed, such cross-connections are present in enormous profusion. In insects they are found in the ganglia, or nerve centres, that lie immediately behind the eye. In higher animals, not only are the nerve cells immediately in front of the sensory cells interconnected but also other cells that lie deeper down in the nervous system.

But there is even more to movement than that: what about speed of movement? Clearly this is important—and indeed animals at times do react differently to objects that move at different speeds. Often they can even discriminate between a smooth movement and a wavy or an irregular one. How the nervous system achieves this, however, is as yet unknown.

Another complex aspect of vision is the distinction and recognition of shapes. It is quite easy to train a bird or a mammal to respond to a circle and to ignore a rectangle—I have myself derived much enjoyment from studies of such form discrimination in wasps. The female digger-wasp, who stocks her burrow with insects she has killed as food for her larvae, clearly has this ability. The question is, how does she manage to find her way back from some distant hunting ground to her own burrow in a large colony? I soon found that these wasps remembered the arrangement of small landmarks such as pebbles, pine-cones and tufts of grass around their burrows. Knowing this, I trained wasps to recognize a circle of pine-cones which I laid out around the entrance. When such a wasp went foraging, I moved this circle a foot or so. The result was that when she returned she searched vainly for her burrow in the centre of the ring of cones, ignoring the real entrance which was in plain view. In subsequent tests, I offered her a choice between a circle of dark stones and a triangle or an ellipse of pine-cones. Although she could distinguish the stones from the cones

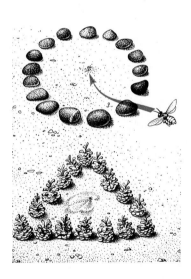

THE CONFUSED DIGGER-WASP

A digger-wasp always memorizes the landmarks around its burrow so that it will be able to find its way back. In an experiment to test this, Dr. Tinbergen surrounded a burrow with a ring of pinecones (top), and the wasp immediately learned to recognize it. But when the ring was moved a foot or two (second drawing), the wasp was unable to find its burrow just outside the ring. When the pine-cones were arranged in a triangle and a decoy ring of pebbles was made (third drawing), the wasp chose the pebbles, proving that it was their arrangement rather than the cones themselves that the insect was responding to.

perfectly well, as I knew from other tests, she went to the stone circle—just because it was a circle.

This same matter of form discrimination has been studied intensely in a very interesting experimental animal, the octopus. Like all the cephalopods, the octopus has highly developed eyes, in many respects similar to the lens eyes of vertebrates. It distinguishes well between shapes and can easily be trained to come forward, preparing to feed, when specific shapes are shown. It has no difficulty in telling a vertical from a horizontal rectangle. However, it gets confused when presented with two oblique rectangles, one held at right angles to the other, or with a V-like and a W-like figure. It looks as if in shape recognition a process is involved in which the vertical and horizontal projections of the different shapes are compared to each other—as if some kind of central nervous scanning of the retina takes place.

WHAT THE OCTOPUS SEES

Experiments with octopuses have revealed the interesting fact that they can distinguish between certain shapes but not between others. This was tested by fastening each of the four shapes below to a stick and presenting them, with crab attached (above), to attract the octopus. The animal quickly learned to associate these shapes with food. The next step was to introduce a mild electric shock to the vertical bar (below, left) but not to the horizontal one. The octopus soon learned to tell them apart and to avoid the electrified one. However, it never did learn the difference between the inverted V and the M. Is this due to lack of intelligence on the octopus's part? See the diagrams on the opposite page for the answer.

GOOD   POOR

SENSE organs that respond to touch, to pressure or to other mechanical action are an important part of the basic sensory equipment of most animals. In their simplest forms, they occur in the skin, where they are obviously useful in maintaining a close contact with the surrounding environment. But mechanical stimuli of other kinds are used for many other, far more specialized purposes. By the tension of some muscles, by the laxness of others, by the position of his bones, tendons and joints, a human being gets a constant stream of enormously detailed and useful information about his posture and his movements—as is the case with all higher animals, which have highly complex sense organs in their muscles, tendons and joints. Insects, which have an external skeleton, have other arrangements for the same purposes. Pads of sensory hairs and groups of minute dome-shaped organs are often found at the joint of a leg segment. In the normal position these hairs touch the next segment in such a way that any bending of the joint will move or bend the hairs slightly, triggering a response in the sensory nerves.

The organs sensitive to touch report mechanical stresses due to gravity on the insect's body and allow it to perceive its own weight, or even that of a load when it stands, and to feel when it hangs upside down. Web spiders use this same ability, but with a different mechanism, to locate an insect caught in their web: pulling with their legs at the strands, they can feel the direction which offers the most resistance.

Staying right side up in their world is a problem common to all animals, and here, too, the sense of touch and pressure is involved. Ingenious modifications of the touch organs are used to determine the direction of gravity. In vertebrates, this is accomplished by one or more tiny, hard, pebble-like bodies, called otoliths, in the inner ear. Heavier than the surrounding tissue, the otoliths rest on a cushion of sensory hairs, to which they are attached by a layer of mucus. When the animal is tilted the hairs are bent in one direction or another, and this acts as the stimulus. In many crustaceans the otolith is not formed by the animal itself but consists of a grain of sand that the animal picks up and inserts every time it sheds its shell. Alois Kreidl, a resourceful Austrian zoologist of the 19th century, demonstrated the function of this grain of sand in a most ingenious and interesting fashion. He put a shrimp in an aquarium on a bed of iron filings instead of sand. When it moulted, the unfortunate animal ended with a grain of iron in its gravity organ, and when a strong magnet was held over it, it swam upside down.

Some aquatic insects keep their balance in the water in still another way.

They carry next to their bodies a small supply of air, held in place by a coat of water-repellent hairs. The spaces between the hairs are not large enough to let the air escape, but they do permit direct contact between the air bubble and the surrounding water. With an "air pocket" like this on each side of its body, such an insect can tell if one side is tipped down, because the side that is deeper in the water will be subjected to a very slightly increased pressure. This compresses the air in the bubble, permitting the water to press slightly farther into the pocket; sensitive hairs detect this and relay the information to the insect that it is no longer horizontal.

Insects also depend on sensory hairs for other kinds of information—picking up minute vibrations in the water, for example. A water bug, *Notonecta*, finds its prey this way. Hanging upside down from the surface, it uses the hairs on its long, delicate legs to detect ripples sent out by other tiny swimmers or struggling insects which have fallen into the water. In an aquarium, *Notonecta* can be stimulated to swim towards a thin wire held on the water surface and vibrated gently so as to send out little ripples. It is amazing how accurately these insects can aim for the source of the ripples by this seemingly primitive mode of orientation, and this without the aid of any visual guide.

The whirligig beetles have gone one better than *Notonecta*. They are surface swimmers, and as they glide about on ponds they rest their feelers just on top of the water. These feelers are equipped with pads of sensory hairs which detect not only surface ripples made by other moving insects but even the presence of motionless objects such as rocks or floating pieces of wood nearby—the water bug apparently has the ability to register the echoes of its own ripples bouncing off these obstacles.

The principle of echo location is carried to extraordinary lengths by the finest specializations of the mechanical senses we know: the organs of hearing. Hearing itself is already astonishing enough, and it may be appropriate to pause here for a few words about it. What we recognize as "sound" is actually the creation of pressure waves in a medium like air or water by some kind of movement. If a tuning fork is struck, its ends will vibrate and this vibration affects the surrounding air, sending rapidly alternating waves of high and low pressure out into the room. When these waves hit a membrane like the ear-drum, it will vibrate also, and these signals, sent to the brain, are recognized as sounds. The diaphragm in a telephone receiver is simply a vibrator, sending sound waves to our ears; so is a radio loud-speaker.

N oт all ears are membranes. Mosquitoes hear with plumes on their antennae. Many locusts have "ear-drums" on their legs; nocturnal moths often have them on the sides of their bodies. In general, insect ears are far less elaborate than the ears of vertebrates; for one thing, they seem unable to distinguish pitch. Yet they are very sensitive to differences in sound intensity, and they utilize to the full the rhythmic properties of sound pulses. The males of the grasshopper *Ephippiger* perform a rhythmic staccato song to attract females: this song can be successfully imitated with sounds of any pitch within their range of hearing, but only when these sounds either begin or end abruptly. A tape recording of a long, smooth whistle elicits no response whatever from the females, but if the tape is cut in two just at the peak of the sound, thereby breaking it off abruptly, and the two parts are linked by a piece of blank tape, either of the two halves will make the female approach.

Sensitivity to the various parts of the sound spectrum differs for different in-

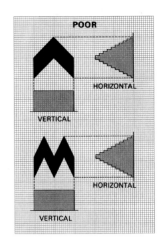

It is not lack of intelligence that handicaps the octopus, but limitations of its eye, which can scan an object vertically and horizontally to measure its dimensions rather than its precise shape. To see what this means to the octopus, it is necessary to make projections of the four objects. In these graphs each dimension is measured by the number of small background squares that any part of one of the objects covers. For example, the very top of the inverted V covers only 1 square. At its centre it is 20 squares wide, and at its bottom it again covers only 1 square. A horizontal projection of this comes out as a triangle (in colour), 1 square wide at its top, 20 wide in the middle and decreasing again to 1 square at the bottom. Wherever the V is measured vertically it is 10 squares thick, and thus the vertical projection is a rectangle, also 10 squares thick (shown in colour). The same is true of the M; its projections are identical with those of the V, and the two are indistinguishable to the octopus. However, the projections of the two other shapes (below) are different, and the octopus can tell them apart.

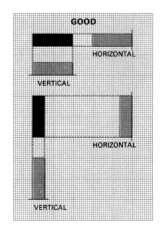

sects—and some can hear in the ultrasonic range. Just as bees can see ultra-violet light, moths can hear ultrasonic sound—an adaptation to detect their enemies the bats, whose calls are largely ultrasonic.

Vertebrates, for the most part, hear very well. Even the fishes, which were thought until fairly recently to be quite deaf, not only have a well-developed hearing sense but also communicate by sounds. Frogs and toads, many reptiles, and of course birds and mammals, all produce a bewildering variety of sounds without which the countryside would seem very desolate indeed. Most of these sounds act as social signals, and most of them indicate a good ability to discriminate pitch.

The champions of hearing, by any standard, are the bats. Bat sounds long went undetected because they are pitched two to three octaves above what we can hear. Very few human ears can detect air vibrations with frequencies higher than some 20,000 per second, and the average limit of human hearing is down near to 14,000 cycles. Bats, however, produce and hear sounds of up to and over 100,000 vibrations per second. Moreover, these sounds are very loud: if we were able to hear them, they would sound like the scream of a jet fighter at close range. To a number of bats flying around on a calm, still summer evening, and to the unfortunate moths which can hear them and must try and avoid them, the evening is anything but calm. It is an inferno of constant shrieking, each bat emitting a series of screams in extremely short pulses of less than a hundredth of a second in duration.

What is important to the bat is not the sound but its echo: bouncing off obstacles like trees, walls and even flying insects, this keeps the bat informed, as sonar does a submarine, of things in its way and food on the wing. This echo-location device has evolved in different bats in different ways—some send out a wide, scattered beam, others a narrow one which can be changed in its direction and thus used as a scanning device. We know that the mechanics of this involves the bats' ears, mouth and, in some species, nose, because if any of these are blocked, they fly "blind". But how the bats' ears and brains process the information they receive from the echoes is still a mystery—their auditory apparatus must be of great complexity.

WHALES use a similar sonar system in the water. It has long been known that whales could hear—readers of *Moby Dick* will recall that sperm-whales must be approached very quietly—and it is also no news that they make sounds. British sailors called one particularly articulate species, the arctic beluga whale, the "sea canary". But the full story was not revealed until World War II, when hydrophones, developed for the detection of submarines, picked up the amazing variety of under-water noises which are produced by whales and dolphins. We know now that at least some whales can emit ultrasonic sounds as high as those of bats, although we still do not understand how they produce them, since they have no vocal cords. We know also that they use echo location for avoiding obstacles and for finding prey, and that they have a vocal "language" for social communication.

Further investigations like those already conducted with porpoises in the Marineland aquaria of Florida and California may reveal still other aspects of whale life. For instance, it may explain the puzzling phenomenon of mass strandings and deaths of whales in shallow water. For many years nobody could understand why these huge creatures sometimes came into shallows, got stuck there and died of suffocation when the weight of their bodies, no longer

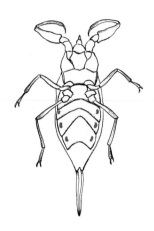

TELLING UP FROM DOWN

The adult water scorpion, Nepa, determines its position in the water by means of small holes on its belly. The openings of these holes are covered by membranes, which are pushed in or out very slightly by expansion and compression of air in the holes—according to how deep in the water the holes are. In the enlargement below, the upper hole, near the scorpion's head, is subject to less water pressure than the lower one, near its tail. The slight disturbance of the membranes covering the holes informs the scorpion that it is headed up towards the surface.

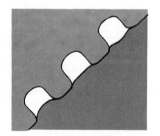

supported by the water, made it impossible for them to inflate their lungs properly. Now it has been pointed out that strandings occur almost always on gently sloping sandy or muddy bottoms, precisely the places where the coastline would fail to give exact echo-location information such as the whales would get on steeper rocky coasts.

Still very mysterious are the lateral line organs possessed by many fishes and some frogs. These are made up of pits or grooves arranged along the body surface, each containing rows of sensory cells. From each cell protrude protoplasmic "hairs" which respond to the slightest movements of the surrounding water—such as might be caused by the approach of a prey or another fish. The hairs are extremely sensitive and, like ears, can receive information from distant objects. Because of their great sensitivity, excessive stimulation may be actually painful —many territorial fish ward off intruders with strong beats of their tails which, without touching them, may be as effective as direct blows.

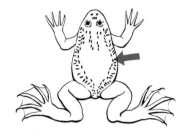

JUST as all sound- and echo-locating devices are basically mechanical, the qualities of smell and taste are often lumped together as the chemical senses. Smell is generally used for preliminary examination of things, sometimes at a distance; taste for things actually touched, as food is tasted when it is in the mouth. The distinctions between smell and taste blur when we consider the chemical sensitivity of the lower animals, but very many of them do have a chemical sense for distance perception and another for the final check of food before it is swallowed.

It comes as no surprise to learn that many animals have better chemical sense organs than we have and that they use them in quite a different way. Even among our close relatives, the mammals, we cut a poor figure. The world of smells in which a dog must live would be bewildering to a human—a good tracking dog can follow a single scent through a mixture of other scents with uncanny certainty. Mammalian predators use smell extensively for tracking their prey; and the preyed-upon to avoid their hunters. One animal less well endowed may even make use of a superior nose belonging to another. It is a common sight in the African savannah to see baboons and impalas travelling together, the impala profiting from the baboon's keen eyesight, the baboon from the impala's sense of smell.

Most commonly—and quite logically—the sense of smell in vertebrates is located near the front end, in the nose. This may be supplemented by another sensing device known as Jacobson's organ, common among many reptiles. Jacobson's organ is actually a small cavity in the head; it has no external opening, but opens into the roof of the mouth. Whether it should be called a tasting or a smelling organ is difficult to say, emphasizing again the fact that these two senses overlap somewhat in most animals, since they both depend on chemical analysis. Jacobson's organ is lined with sensing cells which "smell" by responding to molecules in the air. The reason a snake constantly flicks out its forked tongue is that it is testing the air, collecting a small sample on its tongue, which is then brought back into the mouth and inserted into Jacobson's organ for analysis. Newts have no such tongues but, being amphibians, have evolved noses that can be used both in the air and under water.

A sense organ which is entirely alien to us is associated with the curious electric "battery" found in some fishes. The fact that certain species, like the electric eel of South America, can deliver powerful electric shocks as a means of defence against predators and of stunning prey has long been known, but it

TELLING FRONT FROM REAR

The sides of the African clawed frog are equipped with "lateral buds", shown above as small specks. These are pit-like organs lined with microscopic hairs which bend in response to movements of water along the frog's body. The buds "fire" impulses into the nervous system, and the rate of firing varies according to whether the surrounding water is moving from front to rear along the frog's skin, standing still or moving from rear to front (graphs A, B and C respectively, below). So sensitive are the buds that they can also detect slight disturbances in the water made by insects and wrigglers, which the frog can catch even when blindfolded.

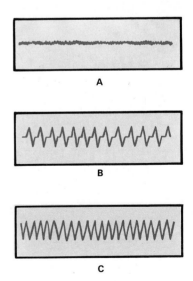

A

B

C

is only quite recently that scientists have realized there is more to the electric organs than that. They are now considered to be extreme specializations of much more common organs which create very weak electric currents and are used to locate obstacles and prey. In other words, the "sixth sense" possessed by such fishes is a high degree of sensitivity to electrical fields.

An outstanding example of this is an African fresh-water fish, *Gymnarchus niloticus*, which has a set of muscles in its tail that have lost the power to contract. Instead, they send out a continuous stream of weak electric discharges, at a rate of about 300 per second. During each discharge, the tail is momentarily electrically negative with respect to the head of the fish. Thus the fish generates in its environment a two-poled field of electric current, and it can sense weak disturbances in this field. The sense organs are located in and near the head and consist of pores in the thick skin, which itself is non-conducting. These pores lead into jelly-filled channels. At the bottom of these channels are found groups of sensory cells which have elaborate nerve connections with the brain. It is possible to train such fish to discriminate between a non-conducting object, such as a piece of glass suspended in the water, and an identically shaped conducting object, such as a porous tube filled with a salt solution or with acid. These objects distort the electric field around the fish in different ways, and the fish can feel these differences on the surface of its body. The physiology of these sense organs is still not quite known, but their extreme sensitivity is already clearly proved.

With this apparatus, *Gymnarchus* cannot detect fish that are more than four inches away from it. However, distance is not particularly important, since these fish live in densely populated and turbid waters where visibility is very poor— also they are nocturnal.

THIS brief review cannot possibly provide more than a glimpse into the fascinating world of the senses. There are certainly more sense organs than I have mentioned. Some marine animals, for instance, respond to slight differences in salinity. Other animals can detect differences in the humidity of the air; bees use this ability to find their way to the nectar in a flower, and lizards to find their way to water. Many animals perform feats of orientation that still baffle the scientist. No one has yet been able fully to explain homing in birds or the migration of marine fishes. And there are many lower animals in the sea that apparently sense differences in the tides, spawning only during spring tides, or full moon and new moon tides. How they can tell which is which we do not know—perhaps they register subtle fluctuations in pressure, which would be greatest during spring tides.

And what about perception that goes beyond the senses that we know? This is called extrasensory perception, and it is an issue blurred by various factors, of which imprecise terminology is one. If one defines a sense organ as any organ that provides an animal with information about the outside world, there is per definition no such thing as extrasensory perception. On the other hand, if one applies the term to perception by processes not yet known to us, then extrasensory perception among living creatures may well occur widely. In fact, the echo location of bats, the functions of the lateral line in fishes and the way electric fishes find their prey are all based on processes which we did not know about—and which were thus "extrasensory" in this sense—only 25 years ago. There is no point in quarrelling about a term—what we can all agree on is that we must continue our studies of the animal's windows to the world.

44

ALTHOUGH MOST SPIDERS RELY ON TOUCH FOR THEIR INFORMATION, THE TARANTULA DEPENDS ON ITS BEADY EYES—ALL EIGHT OF THEM

Senses: Means to an End

All animals, from the lowest on the evolutionary scale to the highest, manifest behaviour of some sort. Though all share one world, all may be said to live in different worlds, since each perceives best only that part of the environment essential to its success. Thus, how an animal behaves has much to do with what its sense organs are and whether these are few or many, simple or complex.

Feelers for Smelling, Hairs for Tasting

Although among most animals the head serves as the repository of the major sense organs, there are many in which some or all of these organs must lie elsewhere—either because the head is too small to contain them or does not exist, or because another

1 Tasting food with the sensory hairs on its feet, a house-fly lets down its elephant-like proboscis and begins to feed. The square shows the area of the proboscis examined in ever finer detail below.

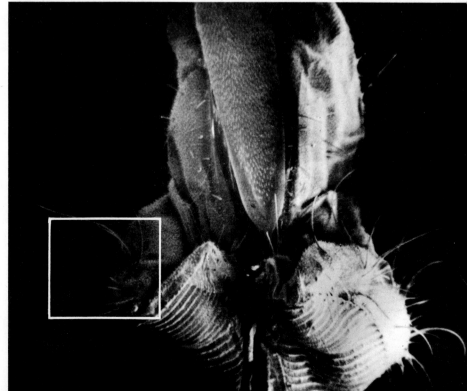

2 Magnified 75 times, the proboscis is shown to have two lobes. The fly eats by pressing the proboscis against food, particles of which are drawn up through pores and the cavity between the lobes.

structure represents a better place for them to be. The headless mussel has developed eyes and tentacles for tasting that lie around the edge of its shell. Some sea snails carry their eyes on their backs, tubeworms have them on the tips of their tentacles.

Grasshoppers hear with organs on their legs or abdomens. Many moths and butterflies smell with their antennae. Flies taste with countless hairs on their legs and must first step on their food (*below*) in order to become sufficiently stimulated to eat it.

3 In a further magnification, the area marked off by a square in the previous picture becomes a forest of sensory hairs, which, like those on its feet, enable the insect both to taste and feel its food.

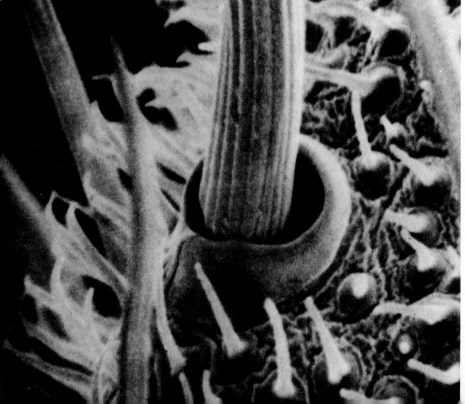

4 Never before seen with such depth of focus, a single sensory hair, magnified here almost 2,600 times by the new scanning electron microscope, rises from its rounded, hollow socket like a sturdy column.

Beyond the Senses of Man

As far as the senses go, the world is not as it seems. Perception must vary from one kind of animal to another, since the sense organs rarely, if ever, have exactly the same range. Take man and bee. Because the human eye reacts to light waves of only a certain length, man fails to respond to the shorter and longer waves of the optical spectrum. The bee is not so hampered—at least as far as the shorter waves go —and can actually see ultra-violet. Thus, to the bee a flower may display a pattern etched in ultra-violet (*left*) that impels the bee towards the nectar. But should the flower be red, the bee would see it as black, simply because its eyes do not register the longer light waves. At the other end of the visible spectrum, where red becomes infra-red, man goes "blind" himself, yet a creature like the diamond-back rattler (*below*) has its own way of perceiving it.

WHAT THE BEE SEES differs from what man sees, as these pictures reveal. In each panel, the flowers are the same, but the ones on the right have been photographed through an ultra-violet filter to show patterns normally visible only to the bee.

THE SCALY HEAD of a diamond-back rattlesnake exhibits uncommon sense organs—a pit beneath each eye that enables the snake to detect its warm-blooded prey through infra-red radiation. Containing numerous, tightly packed nerve endings, the pits respond to heat but not to light, and thus let the diamond-back locate food in the dark, when it usually does its hunting.

WITH A BURST OF POWER of the kind used to kill its prey, an electric eel lights up more than 200 neon bulbs. Set off here by handling, the discharge usually occurs only after a fish swim-ming into the electric field around the eel's body causes a dis-turbance which affects sensory pits in the eel's head. These tell the eel where the fish is, how big it is and whether to fire.

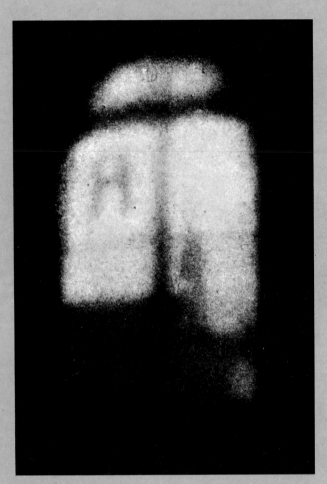

TAKEN THROUGH GLOW-WORM'S EYES, these photographs suggest more about insect vision than they in fact show. The first, made in 1891 by the Austrian physiologist Exner, is of a window, with a letter R pasted on it, and a steeple; the second, made 27 years later, is of a man. Both are, at best, approximations of the images as registered by the insects' retinas.

The Sense of Sight—New Light on an Ancient Subject

Among different animals, different senses dominate. In birds, sight does; in most mammals, smell and hearing do. Fishes can be said to rely upon smell and touch for information about their environment; most insects upon smell and taste. Man uses all these senses, but again, as with other animals, one sense dominates, and this sense, of course, is sight.

Because he leans on sight so heavily, man naturally enough has long tended to consider the world in a visual way; not only has he assumed that most other animals depend on their eyes more than they actually do but he has also assumed that they see the way he does. That accounts for the numerous experiments made with cameras and insect eyes—investigators

thought that if they could take photographs through the eyes, they might see the world as an insect does. Nothing could be further from the truth. What photographs like the ones above really show is not what the glow-worms might have seen, but what the camera saw. How such images would have been processed by the brains of the glow-worms—and how, therefore, they would have been seen by the insects—is simply not known.

Misconceptions about vision can be attributed not only to human bias but to incomplete and often inaccurate information about the different kinds of eyes in the animal kingdom. Man's understanding of even his own eye has been amazingly slow in com-

THE ACTUAL FACETS OF A GLOW-WORM'S EYE—not seen in the old photographs opposite—show up here in a 1963 photograph of a young woman by the science photographer Roman Vishniac. To prepare the eye, Dr. Vishniac had first to clear away all nerves and muscles with tiny needle-like spines from a fresh-water sponge, a task that took about 18 hours to finish.

ing, and for centuries was based upon the false notion, first propounded by the ancient Greeks, that the lens captured the image and that the retina (the true photo-receptor) nourished the lens and conveyed to it, from the brain through the optic nerve, a mysterious power called the "visual spirit". Not until late in the 16th century was the Greek view seriously challenged, by the Swiss anatomist Platter, who proposed that the lens captured light instead and distributed it over the retina. The German astronomer Kepler suggested in 1604 that the image was somehow "painted" on the retina. A few years later a Jesuit friar named Scheiner offered dramatic proof of this—in peeling away the opaque layers at the back of the eye, he actually laid bare an image, a faint, fleeting record of what the eye had been taking in at the moment its owner had died. When, late in the 19th century, it became possible to fix such an image on the retina with chemicals and produce something called an optogram, the notion of the eye as a pin-hole camera gained wide acceptance and persists today. Such a notion, however valid, does nothing to explain what happens to the image once it has fallen on the retina, a fascinating problem that is only just beginning to be solved. Some of the startling discoveries made to date are depicted and explored on the following pages—in several instances for the first time anywhere outside scientific journals.

The Anatomy
of Vision

ONE: THE IMAGE ON THE RETINA

It may never be possible to show exactly what any animal actually sees. But as the paintings on these and the following pages demonstrate, it is possible to show in a schematic way not only what the image falling on the rear wall of the eye or retina may look like in various animals but also how the retina transforms this image into visual information of use to the brain in initiating behaviour.

The eye alone, of course, never sees: the brain sees. What the eye does in its most basic role is to register light. To this end, all eyes, from the simplest to the most complex, have in common light-sensitive cells. These cells, thousands of them packed together, form a sensitive screen in the retina. Light striking this screen excites each cell individually, and together the light-stimulated cells form a mosaic-like pattern, an image of what the eye is looking at.

This, the first major step in the process of vision, is the subject of the paintings at the right. What the animal will ultimately see (*shown on the following pages*) depends on how its retina and brain process the mosaic. Here are shown the three kinds of image-forming eyes that have evolved in the animal kingdom, each looking at the same starlike shape from the same distance. The paintings at the bottom are enlargements of the light-sensitive portion of each eye on which the image is recorded. In the first two, the tiny squares represent the individual receptors; in the third, the facets do.

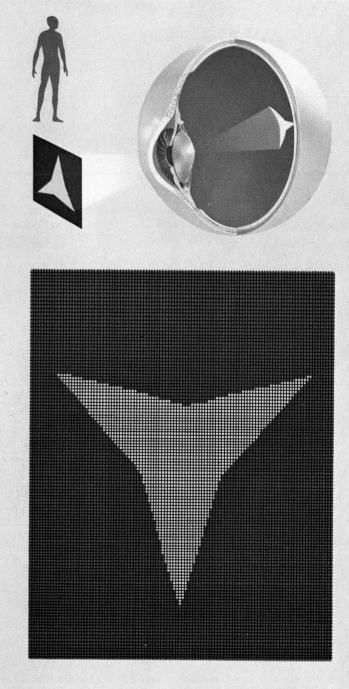

THE HUMAN EYE, which stands here also for the eyes of other vertebrates, is like a camera, with a diaphragm (the iris) to regulate the amount of light passing into it through the pupil, an elastic lens to focus the light, and film (the receptors of the retina) to record the light. Although far from perfect optically, it is superior to the eyes of many other vertebrates. The human eye is characterized by its receptors, some 130 million tightly packed rods and cones which connect to about one million optic nerve fibres. The image they form (*above*) shows a remarkable fineness and appear as one piece when reassembled in the brain, although in fact it is a mosaic on the retina.

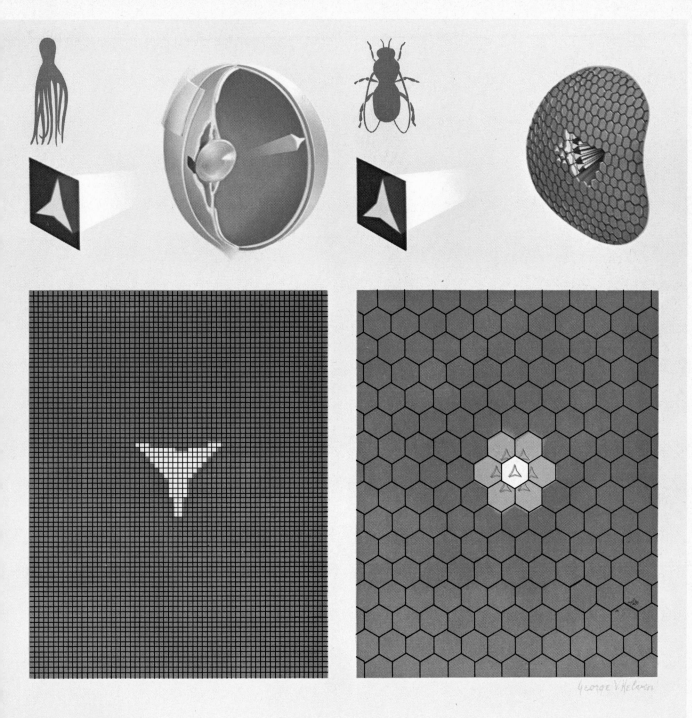

THE OCTOPUS EYE, the most advanced visual apparatus of any found among the invertebrates, has evolved independently of the vertebrate eye, yet, with a few obvious differences such as a rectangular pupil and two protective coats instead of one, it shares many of its basic features. Here again the eye operates on the principle of a camera. However, the image, as registered by the receptors (*above*), is smaller—because the eye itself is smaller. It is also much less precise, not because of any inability of the muscle-controlled lens to focus clearly, but because the receptors are fewer in number and proportionately bigger—and thus produce a coarser mosaic.

THE INSECT EYE—the so-called compound eye—consists of many tiny units, each of which may be said to be an eye in itself, since each has its own lens and light-sensitive cells connected to the brain. These little "eyes" may number from less than 12 in some cave-dwelling insects to more than 28,000 in the dragon-fly. Because of their tapered shape, they face outwards in slightly different directions, and thus each takes in a different part of the scene. The painting above shows how the facet aimed directly at the starlike shape receives the complete image, while the surrounding facets receive only part of it —a result of their not being aimed exactly at the star shape.

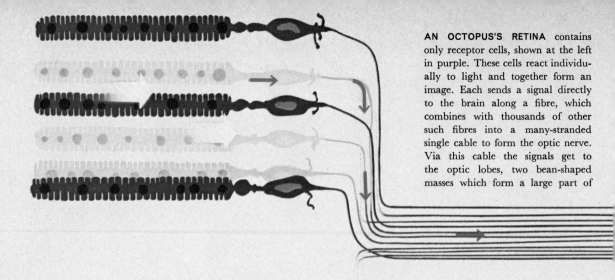

AN OCTOPUS'S RETINA contains only receptor cells, shown at the left in purple. These cells react individually to light and together form an image. Each sends a signal directly to the brain along a fibre, which combines with thousands of other such fibres into a many-stranded single cable to form the optic nerve. Via this cable the signals get to the optic lobes, two bean-shaped masses which form a large part of

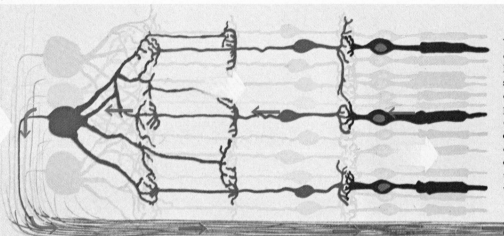

THE FROG'S RETINA is much more complicated than the octopus's. It has three layers of nerve cells instead of one: an inner layer of receptors (*purple*), a middle layer of bipolar cells (*blue*) and an outer layer of ganglion cells (*pale green*). Light entering the eye (*yellow arrows*) does not activate the outer layers, but does activate the receptors, which initiate signals that travel in the direction of the red

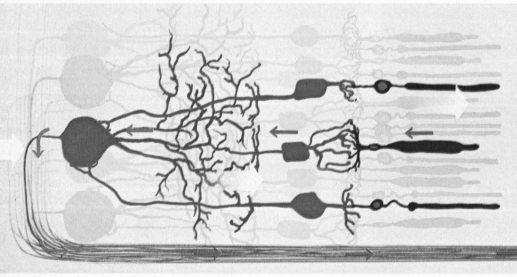

THE CAT'S RETINA, oddly enough, has only two kinds of ganglion cells, as opposed to four kinds for the frog, although its owner is a more highly developed vertebrate. A way to characterize it would be to describe it as less orderly—the ganglion cells display an almost haphazard connection to the bipolar cells. Even so, the nerve impulses coming from the receptors follow the same basic route to the brain.

VISION, TWO: THE EYE AND THE BRAIN

The recording of an image on the retina, as has already been shown, is but the first step in vision. The second step involves getting the image to the brain in useful form. These diagrams show in broadest outline how this is accomplished in an invertebrate (an octopus) and two vertebrates (a frog and a cat). The octopus has a relatively simple retina, consisting of a single layer of receptor cells which transmit visual information directly to the brain for processing. The frog and the cat—in fact, all vertebrates—

the octopus's brain. Here the signals, or visual information, are processed and, in ways as yet unknown, put to use by the octopus. The octopus is able to see remarkably well because of the high development of its eyes and central nervous system. It can also distinguish between shapes, which, considering the limited amount of visual interpretation that the average invertebrate can make, is amazing.

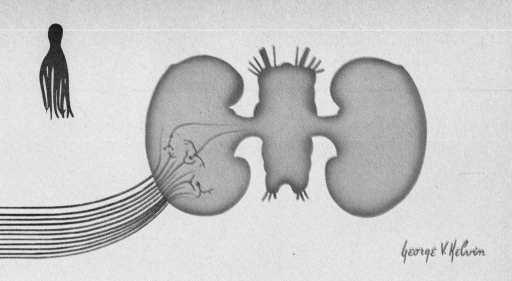

George V. Kelvin

arrows—back through the bipolar and ganglion cells and via the optic nerve to the brain. Reflecting the importance of speed to the insect-eating frog, nine-tenths of the visual information gets processed right in the retina and is then forwarded directly to a reflex centre in the brain (*orange*), where it is acted upon almost at once. Is it any wonder that the frog has been described as a living catapult?

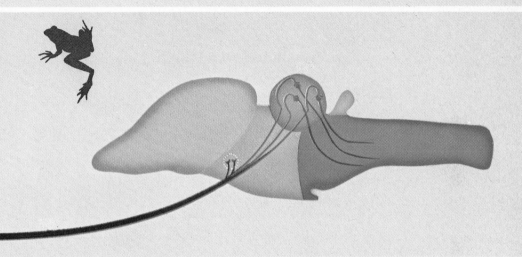

But something different happens to the impulses when they reach the brain. Only one-tenth go to a reflex centre like that of the frog. The other nine-tenths connect to cells in a kind of relay station (*dotted circle, blue*), before being sent on for final processing to the cerebral cortex. This arrangement would apparently give the cat a broader choice in responding to what it sees than the reflex-dominated frog.

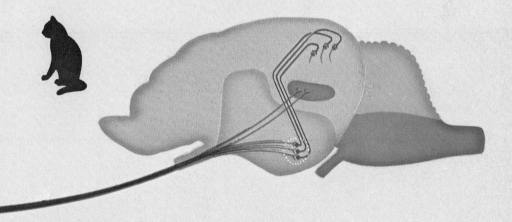

have much more complicated retinas, made up of three separate layers of nerve cells. Light entering the eye passes right through the cells of the first two layers, without affecting them, on its way to the receptors at the back. Here it triggers nerve impulses —electrical signals which pass from the receptors to the bipolar cells for initial processing and then on to the ganglion cells for further processing, and finally along the fibres that form the optic nerve to the brain for still further processing. Some details of how this processing is carried out in both the retina and the brain are shown on the next pages.

VISION, THREE: LAYERS OF THE RETINA

The vertebrate retina is characterized by its complexity. The painting on the right is a highly magnified cross-section of a frog's retina, showing the three layers of cells already described: receptors (*purple*), bipolar cells (*blue*), and the ganglion cells (*various colours*). The receptors are the only cells sensitive to light; the bipolar cells are essentially links between the receptors and the ganglion cells. However, their linkages vary—some of them connect with one receptor, some with several; some of them meet the ganglion cells half way, others send fibres almost to the bodies of the cells themselves. These variations in linkage are believed to make possible the first step in processing the visual information, much as the wiring in radio controls the nature of the signal which travels through it.

There are even greater differences of size and of structure among the ganglion cells than among the bipolar cells. The type shown in red, for example, is relatively scarce but has a huge network of far-reaching branches which connects up with a great many bipolar cells and thereby enables it to collect information from a large area of the retina. Although the orange type connects with bipolar cells at two levels, it receives information from a more restricted area. The tan type, which also connects to the bipolar cells at two levels, is more numerous than the orange type but receives information from an even smaller area. And the green type, the most numerous of all, receives information from the smallest area.

The effect of this complex circuitry is astonishing: it permits the four kinds of ganglion cells to take the visual information coming from the receptors and to analyse it in four different ways. The red type, for example, seems to fire only when there is a decrease in light—a dimming or darkening of whatever the eye is observing—and thus presumably it conveys to the brain information about large, dark shapes. The orange kind is believed to respond to fairly big moving objects, and the tan to smaller moving objects with curved or pointed edges, such as insects or the tips of wind-tossed grass. The green is activated only by abrupt, contrasting edges of light and dark.

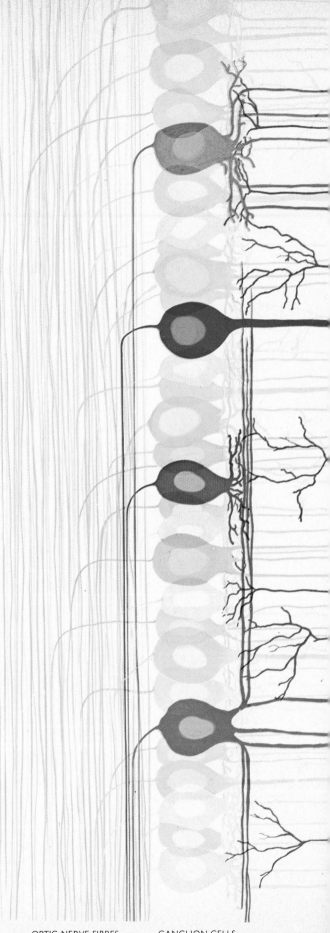

OPTIC NERVE FIBRES   GANGLION CELLS

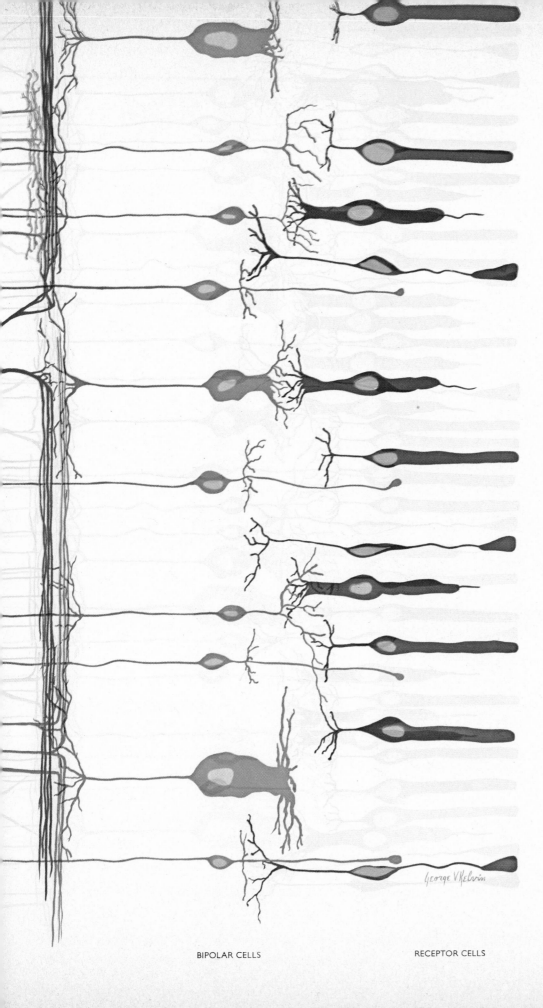

The enlarged portion of the frog's retina at the left in colour is, in reality, infinitesimally small; so small, in fact, that it would easily fit into the tiny square in the drawing of the frog's eye above, with plenty of room left over.

George V. Kelvin

BIPOLAR CELLS   RECEPTOR CELLS

FROG·GANGLION CELLS

Red ganglion cells, largest and least numerous of the four kinds, are affected by dimming; they respond only to darker parts of the swamp scene, such as shadows. Although it is known where they terminate, it is not yet known how the connecting brain cells react.

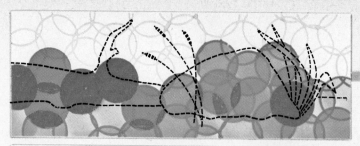

Orange ganglion cells, called "event detectors", become activated when movement occurs in the frog's visual field. Here they respond to the swaying reeds and the grass.

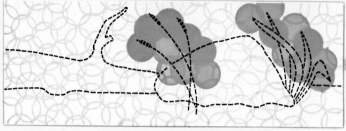

Tan ganglion cells are set off by very small, moving objects with convex edges, like the tips of the cat-tails and grass, and also insects —hence their name: the "bug detectors".

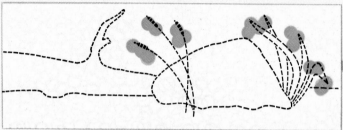

Green ganglion cells, the so-called "edge detectors", react to sharp edges, either lighter or darker than the background. They are shown here outlining the swamp scene. As in the red cells, the response of the connecting brain cells has not yet been determined.

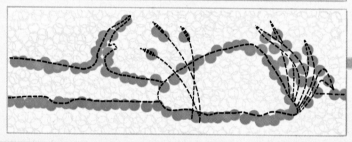

CAT GANGLION CELLS

The retina of a cat contains only two kinds of ganglion cells. One kind, shown here in blue, responds to increases in light. The other, shown in purple, responds to decreases. In short, as long as the light falling on individual receptor cells in the retina is *changing*, one or the other kind of ganglion cells will fire. A steady rate of firing is ensured for the cat by a constant, almost imperceptible tremor in its eye. This tremor causes the image to flick to and fro on the receptors, and these, in turn, react to the changing intensities of light falling on them.

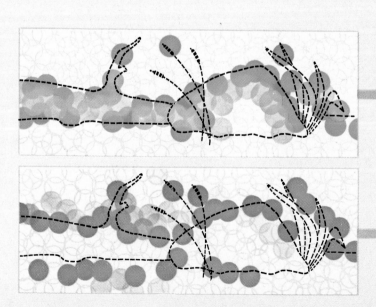

George V. Kelvin

CAT AND FROG WILL SEE THIS SCENE DIFFERENTLY

VISION, FOUR: THE FINAL PROCESSING

We have been talking for six pages about visual processing. What is it? It can best be explained by taking what has already been learned about the four kinds of ganglion cells in the frog's retina and applying it to an actual scene. How these cells might respond to the rock, log and grasses in the landscape above is shown at the left. How cells in the frog's brain might react to the visual information sent from the retina is shown directly below. The same thing can be done for a cat (*lower half of both pages*), which, by contrast, has only two kinds of ganglion cells but many more kinds of brain cells concerned with vision than the frog has. The diagrams for both cat and frog, showing the responses of hundreds of cells at one time, are abstracted from readings made in the laboratory, with electrodes so fine that they could be inserted into single nerve fibres in the optic nerves and brains of living animals.

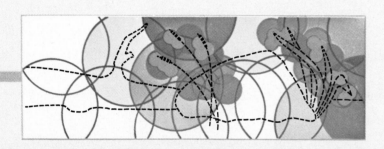

FROG BRAIN CELLS

In the frog's brain, impulses coming from the "event detectors" and the "bug detectors" end up being processed together by large brain cells (*pink circles*), which provide a brand new kind of visual information. What happens to the impulses of the other two kinds of cells at their terminals in the brain is unknown, and thus cannot be depicted.

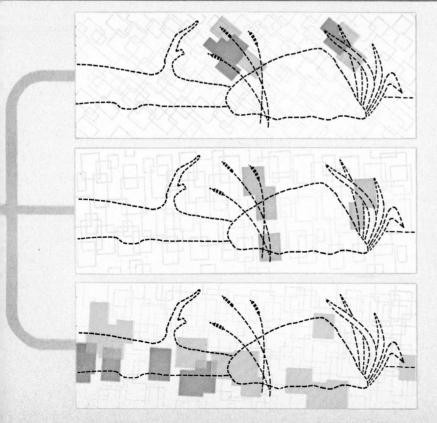

CAT BRAIN CELLS

In the cat's brain, hundreds of different kinds of cells sort out the visual information relayed from the retina. Only three kinds are shown here. The cells in the first two diagrams are concerned with the movement of long, narrow shapes—like that of the waving grasses. Their responses, as these diagrams show, differ slightly from each other. The responses of any other similar cells will also differ, since each cell works on the same visual stimulus from a slightly different angle. Altogether they provide a detailed view of the movement of the grass blade. It is thought that this kind of multiple processing by the brain makes the cat's vision a much more supple and subtle process than the frog's.

The third diagram illustrates brain cells that fire on receipt of information pertaining to edges—either darker edges (*coloured brown*) or lighter edges (*coloured yellow*). All the cat's brain cells are depicted as being rectangles because they actually respond to areas of this shape in their field of vision.

A WELTER OF LURES surrounding a black bass indicates the lengths to which lure makers will go—hoping to stumble on what attracts a bass. If this could be determined scientifically, then a supernormal lure could be designed that might stimulate the fish into biting every time.

3

Stimuli— and What They Do

WHEN I am engrossed in a book or thinking about tomorrow's work, I may fail to hear the clock in my room tick. Yet if you were to ask me whether the clock had stopped, I would switch my attention to it and probably hear it tick very clearly.

Everyone has experienced this kind of thing, and if you stop to think about it the obvious conclusion is that one does not always make use of all the information one's sense organs can provide. Something very similar is true of animals. Early in this century, a famous scientist, Carl von Hess, concluded that all honey-bees are colour-blind: when he took them into the laboratory and confronted them with two lights, they always went to the brighter of the two, regardless of the colours used. The conclusion seemed valid enough—after all, the bees were reacting just like colour-blind people, who discriminate between brightnesses rather than colours of light.

But was it really a valid conclusion? Karl von Frisch, at that time a young research worker, did not think so. For all the great respect and admiration he had for his senior colleague, he had still greater respect for the adaptedness of living organisms—he felt there must be some function in the bright colours of the flowers. To prove this, he conducted a series of experiments with bees in their natural environment, out in a field where they were actually foraging. Instead of lights, he presented them with pieces of cardboard of various colours and also of different shades of grey. The results were clear-cut and convincing: foraging bees did respond to colours, especially to yellow and blue. The bees tested in the laboratory had not been foraging; they had been trying to escape, and in this "motivational state" they became oblivious to colour and reacted only to the brighter light.

We know now that this is only one example of a very widespread phenomenon. Like the professor sitting in his study with the ticking clock, animals do not necessarily use all the potential information about the outside world which their senses are able to give them; what they do use depends on what they are doing at the moment. Therefore, if we want to understand fully how external stimuli help to control an animal's behaviour, we must do more than investigate what they *can* respond to—we must find out what at any given moment they actually *do* respond to. Once again, we must go beyond the seemingly obvious and probe our subject in depth—in this case, exploring in depth the animal's world of external stimuli.

It is rather remarkable that this has been done so rarely. Yet even on the basis of the relatively few experiments undertaken since we started concentrating on this field, some extremely interesting phenomena and problems have been noted.

**THE SEXUAL RESPONSES
OF THE GRAYLING BUTTERFLY**

In an effort to learn more about how male grayling butterflies respond to females, Dr. Tinbergen and his colleagues worked out some ingenious experiments. These were all based on the male's well-known habit of flying up in pursuit of a passing female and utilized different kinds of "female" models made of paper and presented to the males like lures at the end of a fishing rod. Details of the experiments are shown on the opposite page.

THE grayling butterfly offers an excellent case in point in its sexual pursuit of a female. Males of the species often rest on the bark of trees or on the ground in arid, sandy areas. They are beautifully camouflaged, and it is often rather startling to see one fly up, as it were, out of nowhere—which they do whenever a female flies by. If the female is willing to mate, she will alight; the male then settles near her and starts his ground courtship. But a female that is unwilling flies on, and the male, after following her a few yards, abandons her and settles down to wait for another.

What makes a male fly at a female? This was the key question, and it led us through an amusing sequence of experiments to a rather surprising answer.

Simple observation in the natural habitat gave us the clue to our own line of testing. We soon saw that it was not just the female of the species that stimulated the graylings to rise but also a large variety of other insects ranging in size from small flies to butterflies much larger than the female graylings. We even saw the hapless males rise in pursuit of birds up to the size of thrushes. More striking still, we saw them pursue falling leaves of various sizes, shapes and colours—and not only were leaves pursued but sometimes the shadows they cast on the ground, and even the shadows cast by the pursuing males themselves.

All this bewildering variety of objects which the male graylings apparently took for females of their species suggested two things to us: first, that visual stimuli were important; and secondly, that chemical stimuli were not, for scent could be ruled out on the grounds that the direction of the flights was independent of the wind.

But if the decisive stimulus was a visual one, how to find out what factor of vision—size, shape, colour, action or a combination of any or all of these—was responsible for the graylings' behaviour?

We first prepared a number of paper dummies of butterfly shape which we attached with a yard of thin thread to the end of a slender, three-foot pole. With these "fishing rods" we could make the dummy butterflies do almost anything we wanted, and in our initial series of experiments we made them dance in the air towards a male. This invariably elicited a vigorous response, so we set about elaborating the test still further.

We now prepared a large number of dummies, grouped in series, in which one particular characteristic at a time was varied. One series, for example, consisted of dummies which were identical in all respects except colour. In another, colour and size were constant but the shape varied; in still another it was size that changed. Armed with our rods and our various dummies, we roamed over the countryside searching for male graylings. Whenever one was found, the dummies would be presented, always in a standardized way—i.e., moving in the same way, approaching from the same distance, under similar lighting, with the same speed, etc.—at regular intervals and in irregularly varied sequence. This was an attempt to present to each male all the models under roughly the same circumstances and to record how effectively each model elicited his sexual pursuit response. By doing this for one series after another, we could express the stimulating effect of, say, various colours, shapes, sizes and so on in the percentage of occasions on which a model actually elicited a response.

We ran some 50,000 tests of this nature, using a large number of males found in their natural habitats. It was clear at once that the exactness of the imitation of the female was not an important factor. Even when we glued the wings of a real female on to a dummy, we got no more response than was elicited by a dummy coloured a uniform brown. Dummies of all different colours, in fact, all got a response, but some seemed more effective than others. Curiously enough, however, it was not the natural brown of the female that worked best. Black was even better, and gradually it became clear that the darker the colour of a dummy, the more effective it was. This was confirmed with a series of dummies of various shades of grey: white was least effective, and black was best.

Now what about size? We had made a series of dummies ranging from one-sixth the diameter of a normal female to four and a half times normal size. Male graylings rose in pursuit of all these, but much to our surprise, the larger dummies were more effective than those which were the size of an average female.

So we had established three things: movement was important, dark colours worked best, and the bigger the dummy, the better the response. Now what about the effects of shape?

S HAPE, it developed, seemed of little importance. We offered many dummies of different shapes but with the same surface area—long rectangles, butterfly shapes, circular shapes. The long rectangles were the least effective, but we found that this was not because of the shape, but because they moved differently from the other shapes—they did not flutter as well.

So the next thing we studied was the type of movement. This we did by making the same model move in different ways. As anticipated from earlier tests the dancing movement was twice as effective as a smooth and regular movement.

Finally, we tested the effect of distance. The same dummy was made to dance at varying distances from the males. We tried this with many dummies, both "good" ones and "poor" ones, and we found that the nearer the dummy was to the male, the more responses it got.

Putting all this together gave us a much better understanding of why we had seen males follow birds, falling leaves, shadows and all those many other things which seemed so different from a grayling female. Shape mattered little to the males, nor did colour—what was important was bigness, darkness of tone, near-

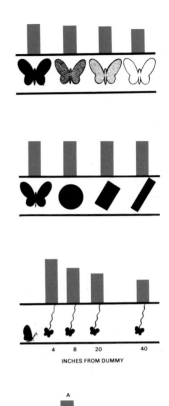

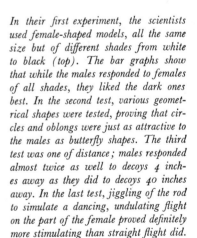

In their first experiment, the scientists used female-shaped models, all the same size but of different shades from white to black (top). The bar graphs show that while the males responded to females of all shades, they liked the dark ones best. In the second test, various geometrical shapes were tested, proving that circles and oblongs were just as attractive to the males as butterfly shapes. The third test was one of distance; males responded almost twice as well to decoys 4 inches away as they did to decoys 40 inches away. In the last test, jiggling of the rod to simulate a dancing, undulating flight on the part of the female proved definitely more stimulating than straight flight did.

ness and a dancing activity. But how did all this add up for the male; in short, how did it say "female"?

The matter seemed inexplicable in human terms, and so we had to consider the possibility that the male graylings "recognized" females in a way quite different from the way humans do. To us, recognition is very often the result of a yes-no decision of some kind: we look at something dancing past and say to ourselves, "this is a female" or "this is not a female". But the butterflies showed no such clear-cut decision. They showed instead a graded scale of responses, as if many of the dummies were to them, let us say, 75 per cent female or 50 per cent female—and the frequency of their responses depended upon the quantity of "femaleness" of the object attracting them.

This opened up an entirely different line of thought—we realized that we had to think not just in terms of stimulation but of *quantity* of stimulation. Both a white and a black butterfly stimulate a male, but the black one stimulates him more strongly than the white one. And we discovered, as we pursued this new line of thought, how curiously automatic this response to strength of stimulation can be. For example, we found that a white dummy, although known to be less stimulating than a black one, would none the less elicit the same number of responses from the males if it was presented from a shorter distance than the black dummy. Similarly, the effectiveness of a white dummy, or a relatively ineffective small dummy, could be boosted by making it dance. So a deficit in one type of stimulus could be compensated for by an increase in another kind of stimulus, however different in kind it might be. It seemed that all the stimuli contributed in a quantitative way to a "pool of stimulation" which caused the grayling to respond.

ANOTHER striking thing was that some properties of the female, such as its colour, did not contribute to this pool of stimulation at all. Did this mean that the males were colour-blind? This was hard to believe—like bees, they feed on flowers whose bright colours would seem to have some function in attracting them. We decided to offer our series of coloured dummies to graylings at a time when they were feeding—and lo and behold, they behaved very differently: they reacted almost exclusively to yellow and blue models. Furthermore, they did not react at all to grey models, showing that they did have true colour vision.

In other words, in the case of the grayling butterfly, whether or not it is stimulated by a coloured object or merely by the darkness of an object depends on what it is doing at the moment. Or, to put the matter in more general terms, the condition of the male decides which part of the outside world it will admit to its pool of stimulation.

Clearly, it would be interesting to see if other animals reacted in this same automatic way. This has been done by studying a variety of behaviour patterns in a number of subjects.

One of these is the feeding behaviour of a large, carnivorous water beetle known as *Dytiscus marginalis*. This beetle preys on fish, aquatic insects, tadpoles and worms, and also occasionally eats carrion. The surprising thing about *Dytiscus* is its clumsiness. Though it has well-developed eyes and obviously good vision, it does not swim straight at its prey; in fact, it does not seem to be able to see it at all. Yet when it is near a prey animal it does show, by changing its normally quiet swimming into a kind of frantic, irregular thrashing, that it has become aware of it. Just what is the stimulus that prompts *Dytiscus* to pursue and devour its food?

We can check this in several ways. First, we can show it a tadpole enclosed in a test tube which we put into the water nearby. The beetle ignores the tadpole completely; it does not even show its frantic swimming movements when it touches the glass. However, if we sew the tadpole into a little bag of cheesecloth which hides it completely from sight, the beetle responds vigorously: it either grabs the bag with its forelegs and begins to chew it up or, if it happens to swim past under the bag, it immediately dives to the bottom and swims around in irregular searching movements below. The same response can be elicited by taking water from a tank in which tadpoles have been swimming and squirting it into the beetle's tank.

OBVIOUSLY, when it is feeding, a *Dytiscus* responds to a chemical stimulus—it smells rather than sees its prey. Yet when it is crawling about on land it uses its eyes to good effect to avoid obstacles, even at a distance and even if these are placed behind glass. By the same token, when it is flying the *Dytiscus* beetle is able to see bodies of water: it often alights on glass, on cars or on other shiny surfaces which it mistakes for water. We can only conclude that a feeding *Dytiscus* just does not use its eyes—here, too, the sensory "input", as it is called, is admitted only in part.

TUNING OUT A STIMULUS

To avoid utter confusion, animals must be able to choose among a great number of sights, sounds and other stimuli pouring into their nervous systems, and select the ones that are most useful to the needs of the moment. A cat sitting quietly will hear the ticking metronome behind it. But if it sees a mouse, the sound of the metronome will no longer register. This can be proved by putting an electrode in the cat's head, wiring this to a meter and observing the response to the regular ticking of the metronome (graph, above), which disappears (graph, below) when the mouse runs by.

This conclusion that an animal does not at any particular moment use all the information its sense organs receive raises an interesting problem: what happens to those stimuli which it does not use? To put it in a slightly different way: when *Dytiscus* is swimming around in bright daylight in search of food, its eyes are stimulated by light; we would expect this input to be carried by sensory nerves to the central nervous system, which, through motor nerves connected with the muscles, would then cause the feeding movements. Yet in a foraging *Dytiscus* the visual stimulus is *not* translated into movement; its feeding movements are unaffected by what it sees. Somewhere along the line between the eyes and the motor centres that control feeding behaviour, the input received by the eyes must be "censored" or suppressed. How is this done?

To answer this question, we have to progress from observation and study of the intact animal to a direct investigation of what is going on inside it. This can be done in various ways. For instance, it can be done in larger animals by sinking extremely fine electrodes into a nerve centre to register the very weak electrical currents generated by external stimuli. Experiments of this kind have been carried out on cats, with an electrode sunk into a nerve centre located directly behind the ear. When a metronome was made to click near the cat, it was possible to see what the cat heard—quite literally, for every time the metronome clicked the nerve centre "fired" and the "action potentials" accompanying the impulses were recorded on the instruments.

Now the cat was shown a mouse. Not surprisingly, its interest at once concentrated on the mouse. But at that same instant, the action potentials registering on the meter disappeared! Yet the metronome was still clicking as before. The cat, however, was now oblivious to what previously it had heard clearly; it had managed somehow to shut out the noise.

Neurophysiologists describe this phenomenon as "gating"—it is as if a gate were opened or closed, either admitting or stopping the flow of information. What is admitted or stopped seems to be determined by what the animal is doing or intending to do—by its motivational state. *Where* and *how* sensory information is stopped in such cases is largely unknown; the example of the cat's ear may or may not be typical.

The cat with the metronome and then the mouse, and *Dytiscus* with the swimming tadpole are reacting to specific stimuli which they select out of a wide range of things assaulting their sensory organs—and these stimuli are sufficiently important to be examined on their own. We call them "sign stimuli". Selective response to sign stimuli is a widespread phenomenon; just exactly how widespread we do not know, and more systematic investigations of the total stimulus situations to which animals react are certainly needed. It is interesting that many animals, even the higher forms, show selective responses to sign stimuli before they can have gained experience with them. This has for instance been studied in detail in newly hatched chicks of the herring-gull.

Normally, as soon as they are hungry, these chicks peck at a red patch near the tip of the lower mandible on the yellow bills of their parents. It is this red patch which very particularly elicits the pecking reaction—a yellow bill without the red patch stimulates only a quarter of the responses that a red-patched bill evokes, and patches of other colours score somewhere in between. Even when one presents the chicks with an array of uniformly coloured bills, all get the same response—except a red bill, which is twice as effective. Yellow, the natural colour of the parents' bills, scores no higher than white, black or blue. But a chick will peck at a red cherry, and I was even told of one case when a fully grown young gull ran up to a little girl at the seashore and pecked vigorously at a "very red scab" on her knee!

This is what we call "misfiring"—an animal's behaviour may go off under inappropriate circumstances and so fail to attain his proper goal. Such misfires often indicate that an animal is responding to a sign stimulus. When songbirds feed a much larger cuckoo chick in their nest while ignoring their own, their behaviour misfires. Our knowledge of sign stimuli makes us understand why this happens: despite the fact that the cuckoo looks so different from the birds' own young, it does provide the part that matters, a particularly large gape showing the brightly coloured mouth and throat that stimulates the parent to feed it. The cuckoo chick, therefore, survives because the song-bird's behaviour is misfiring. By the same token, a moth displaying big "eyespots" on its wings survives because these "eyes" stimulate the song-bird to fright—they alone are the effective stimuli, however different the rest of the moth may be from a predatory mammal or bird.

THE study of stimuli has its eminently practical side, too. In northern Sweden, a valuable salmon fishery was threatened with extinction when a hydroelectric project changed the water level, the vegetation, even the speed of the current in the river the fish habitually spawned in. Under the new conditions, no spawning took place—until a behaviourism student was called in for consultation. He found that the salmon required stretches of gravel in which they could bury their eggs; and not only that, but gravel of a special kind, with stones approximately walnut-sized. Artificial gravel beds were thereupon laid in the river, and this simple measure proved to be all that was needed to save the salmon, and thereby the livelihood of the local fishermen.

The possibilities of applying our growing knowledge of stimulus situations in other fields are obviously great, but to date they have hardly been explored. In most cases where they have been tried, however, they have shown great promise—distress calls of their species, for instance, are much more likely to drive birds away from airfield runways than are moth-balls, and for that matter they have been effective scarecrow substitutes not only in this situation but also in orchards and grain fields. The U.S. Department of Agriculture, for example, has made significant progress in the use of sex and food attractants both to locate and to control destructive insect populations like the gypsy moth in New England and the Mediterranean fruit-fly in Florida.

Most of the experiments on sign stimuli have been carried out with dummies whose design was based on the natural object—the assumption being that the natural object would be the most strongly stimulating one. With this as the standard, the dummies could then be varied in a number of ways to answer the question, How is the object recognized? But once behavourism students began to think in terms of the stimulating effect of single characteristics such as colour, shape and so on, it was natural that they should begin to make the dummies vary beyond the limits of the normal object. Thus, as we have already seen, the grayling male was not by any means most strongly stimulated by dummies of normal female size, but large models were better, while black dummies were more effective than the naturally coloured brown ones. In other words, we have found we can improve on nature; we can provide "supernormal stimulation".

Several such cases have been well studied. Gulls and other birds, if offered the choice between an egg of normal size and an outsize egg, will prefer the latter—only to find that in spite of frantic attempts they cannot even sit on it. Herring-gull chicks, as we have seen, peck at the red spot of the bill of their parent—but further tests showed that this was not a colour stimulus alone but also a matter of contrast. They also pecked at dummy bills showing strongly contrasting patches, like very white on very dark or vice versa. And probing still further, we found that the chicks responded to the shape of the bill: a thin bill was more effective than a thick bill.

With all this information in hand, we decided to try another improvement on nature, so we made a thin rod coloured red, on which we painted three sharply defined white rings. To human eyes this did not look like a good imitation of a herring-gull's bill at all, yet the chicks aimed 25 per cent more pecks at it than at a real herring-gull's bill!

This phenomenon of supernormality may well be more widespread than we realize. For instance, it is possible that many song-birds are not merely *willing* to feed a young cuckoo but simply *love* to feed it, just because the cuckoo offers such an enormous and inviting gape. And the curious fact that several species of hawk moth caterpillars have not one but two eye-spots on each side of the body may have a similar explanation: to the song-birds that prey on them this supernormal arrangement may be more frightening than a normal set of eyes.

Can any of this be applied to man? Since it is not always easy to experiment on our own species, we know less of ourselves than of some animals—but there are many indications that we, too, are sensitive to supernormal stimulation. Many of the animals in the widely beloved cartoons of Walt Disney have "supernormal" baby-faces. Artists painting or sculpting the human body also exaggerate certain aspects deliberately. And what about our responses to lipstick? And our taste responses to salt, to sweet, to hot? What about our response to the flavour of alcohol? It might be worth-while investigating such matters in the same way as we are investigating animals.

Studying the sign stimuli in greater detail, we soon begin to see that neither are they as simple as they appear to be nor is the response of the animal to them, as we might think, as automatic as the response of a slot machine to the weight of a coin. The following story shows how complex a seemingly

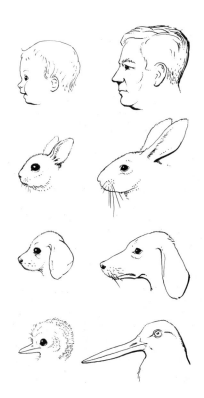

THE APPEAL OF AN INFANT

Does the "baby" look of a baby arouse parental instinct? There seems to be evidence that it does. In the drawing above, the human baby, the bunny, the puppy and the chick all have features, or sign stimuli, that stir up parental feelings: short faces, prominent foreheads, round eyes, plump cheeks. The angular, elongated faces of the adults on the right do not awaken the same feelings. Parental response in humans extends not only towards children but also towards such popular baby substitutes as pets and dolls.

WHERE IS THE HEAD?

Another of Dr. Tinbergen's experiments was aimed at testing visual discrimination in baby thrushes. By presenting the models shown here, he found that they would gape at things that didn't look anything like mother thrushes, but that they nevertheless had an excellent idea of the proper size relationship between a parent's head and body. In the drawing above, for example, the babies gaped to the left towards the small "head" because it seemed the proper size for the "body". But when a larger "body" was presented (below), they switched and gaped at the middle-sized "head", identical with the one they had previously ignored.

simple stimulus can in fact be. Young thrushes, at the age of about 10 days, begin to direct their gaping at the head of the parent bird. It can be easily shown with dummies that the young birds do not react to any specific details of the parent; rather, any slightly moving object close to and above the nestlings makes them gape. Now, let us probe this situation a bit further.

If we use a flat circular disc as a dummy—something that has no top or bottom but will look the same no matter how it is turned—we shall find that the nestlings will gape at its highest part, the part where the parent's head normally ought to be. But if we add a protuberance to the disc, this becomes the head, even if it is placed near the bottom of the disc where no normal head should be. This does not work for any protuberance. Shape does not seem to matter, but size does; and this is most interesting—it is *relative* size, not *absolute* size, that counts. If the "head" is almost as large as the "body", apparently it does not seem like a head and is not as effective as a smaller head would be. This is tested by presenting a disc with two "heads" of different sizes. The nestlings will gape at the most appropriate one, stretching towards the larger of the two heads if they are attached to a large body, and to the smaller one if they are attached to a smaller body.

Such "relational" or "configurational" stimuli seem to be the rule rather than the exception. Relations in space give rise to recognition of form; relations in time to recognition of movement. Both types of relations may be extremely complex. How are sensory data so integrated as to make possible the visual recognition of an individual human face or the aural recognition of a particular melody? So far, no one has been quite able to analyse such matters; yet somehow they are accomplished.

WE BEGAN this chapter by considering what seemed to be a rather simple problem: to which outside stimuli does an animal actually react? We end it on a note of great complexity. We have seen that not all the information which the sense organs can provide is used, that part of the "input" that goes into the animal is somewhere rendered ineffective, depending on what the animal is doing. We have further seen that even the simpler kinds of effective input, the "sign stimuli", are really products of an integrative activity of the animal—in responding to a shape it does more than just sum up the activity of the separate sensory cells; it compares and relates them. So if we want to compare the animal to a slot machine, we may do so—but we must recognize that it is a slot machine of great complexity, in which each coin, or stimulus, causes intense and complicated activity inside it. This becomes even more evident when we realize that the effectiveness of a stimulus depends not merely on the stimulus itself but also on the state the animal is in. And as we shall see, this state changes continually.

Yet, amazing though these perceptual processes are, what the animal finally achieves seems to be much more primitive than what humans do, for, as we have seen, animal behaviour "misfires" much more strikingly than our own behaviour does. But in evaluating this, we must not forget that most of the misfiring occurs when we disturb the normal environment. However risky it would *seem* to rely on sign stimuli, the *actual* risk is not great, and we have to admit that the system works remarkably well. Nor should we think too highly of our own behaviour. An observer from Mars who saw an old spinster kiss her Pekinese might well consider this a striking example of misfiring, and could we honestly say that he would be very wrong?

PECKING INSTINCTIVELY AT A RED SPOT ON ITS PARENT'S BILL, A HUNGRY BABY HERRING-GULL INDUCES THE PARENT TO REGURGITATE FOOD

The Signs of Behaviour

To the chick above, the most important thing in its life at this stage is the red patch on its parent's bill. This is the sign that induces it to peck, and the pecking in turn elicits a feeding response in the parent bird. By just such a system of sign and countersign do many animals act, their behaviour determined by internal need and triggered by information coming to them from the world outside.

FOLD-OUT: DO NOT TEAR

the other stickleback. With its domain secure, the male sets about building a nest. First it clears a shallow pit (3). Having collected material with which to fill the pit—generally strands of algae and bits of other weeds—it then swims to and fro over the loose pile (4), secreting a sticky kidney fluid which glues the nest together. This done, it tunnels through the nest (5). Undergoing still another colour change, it is now ready to court a female; its bright-red belly and bluish-white back act as an attracting stimulus for its prospective mate. Stimulated in turn by the female's egg-plump form, the male goes into a zigzag courtship dance (6), during which it may brush the female's belly with its stickles (7). In response to the female's head-up sign of acceptance, it shows the way to the nest. The male indicates the entrance by turning on its side and pointing inside with its snout (8). Once its mate has entered, it hovers overhead, prodding the base of the female's tail

Reading the Signs

A male three-spined stickleback (*top left*, 1), still wearing its protective winter coloration, swims away from a school of males and females to stake out a territory. As it assumes its pre-nuptial colours, it becomes increasingly aggressive, prepared to defend its territory against all other male sticklebacks— and at this stage even against females. Its defences are varied, but here the male has assumed a threat posture (2). This brings its red belly into view, a sign stimulus that intimidates

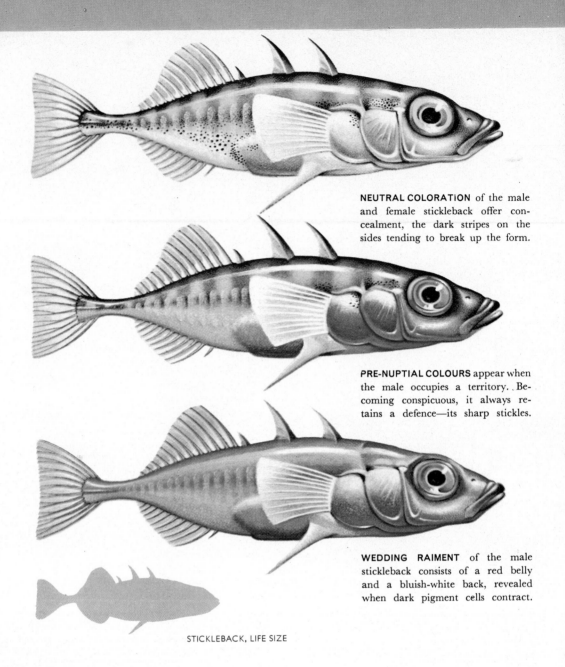

NEUTRAL COLORATION of the male and female stickleback offer concealment, the dark stripes on the sides tending to break up the form.

PRE-NUPTIAL COLOURS appear when the male occupies a territory. Becoming conspicuous, it always retains a defence—its sharp stickles.

WEDDING RAIMENT of the male stickleback consists of a red belly and a bluish-white back, revealed when dark pigment cells contract.

STICKLEBACK, LIFE SIZE

Introducing the Stickleback

To an observer idling at the edge of a pond, the three-spined stickleback might seem like just another small, greyish-green fish, but to those who have studied it in the laboratory, it is a very remarkable fish indeed—one that has helped to unlock several mysteries of animal behaviour. Analysis of its activity during its reproductive cycle revealed the importance of simple stimuli—the so-called sign stimuli—in touching off reactions in both sexes. But before these can take effect, male and female must be ready for reproduction. This happens in the spring, when the gradual lengthening of daylight activates glands secreting reproductive hormones which cause the sticklebacks to migrate from wintering grounds in deep fresh water or the coastal sea to shallow, fresh-water spawning grounds. Here, affected by the change in temperature and motivated by the availability of nesting places, the male changes colour (*above*). Its red belly becomes the first of several "signs" that direct the behaviour of males and females throughout the reproductive cycle, shown on the following pages.

with its snout, which induces spawning (9). When the eggs are laid and the female has slipped out, it enters the nest and fertilizes the clutch (10). After mating with several different females—usually two or three—it begins to fan water over·the eggs to aerate them (11). When the brood hatches a week or so later, the male, once again wearing its protective coloration (12), guards the young. If they roam too far, the father picks up the strays in its mouth and spits them back into the nest.

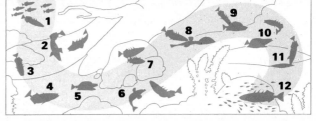

The Triggers of Behaviour

By its very completeness, the study of stickleback behaviour points to the dearth of knowledge about the behaviour of most other animals—and even that of lower organisms as deceptively simple as the one-celled amoeba (*below*). But as research goes on, startling facts keep turning up, showing how many countless responses, previously not understood, may be predicated upon stimuli as elusive as scent molecules or infra-red rays. Scent has enormous importance in releasing behaviour among many insects. Ants, for example, seem to have a whole language made up of odours. Not only do some lay down

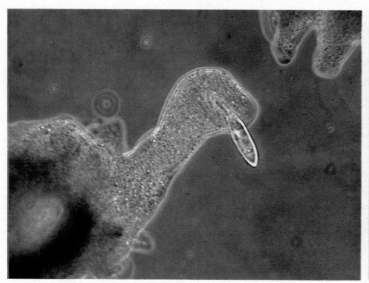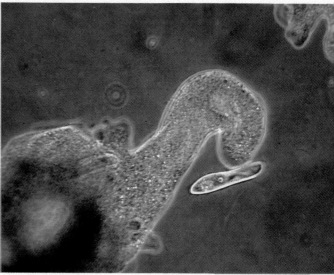

THIS SEQUENCE OF MICROPHOTOGRAPHS SHOWS HOW AN AMOEBA, REACTING TO THE STIMULUS OF FOOD, PUTS OUT FALSE FEET, OR PSEUDOPODS

HELD BY FORCEPS, a male *Lycorea ceres* from Trinidad is shown in three different exposures as it extrudes its hair-pencils—two bundles of hairs on either side of the abdomen which, unfurled, emit a strong, musky perfume. During courtship, the male pursues the female in flight and brushes these pencils over her antennae. Their effect is to induce the female to alight on foliage, where courtship can continue. But since the male also extrudes the pencils when picked up, as here, it has been suggested that they may serve another purpose as well, perhaps startling a predator or repelling it chemically.

chemical trails by which members of a colony can find their way to food, but others emit alarm substances which, transmitted from one worker to the other in a chain reaction, can alert a whole colony to danger. There is reason to believe that the assembling of workers, grooming, food exchange and many other ant activities may also be determined by external secretions. The potency of these chemical stimuli is dramatically suggested by the sex attractant emitted by some female moths. It has been estimated that only .01 microgram of such a substance has the potential to excite a thousand million males.

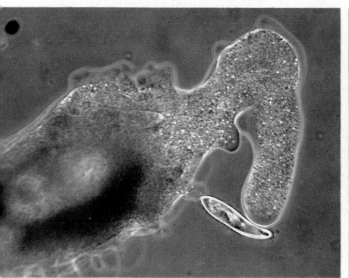 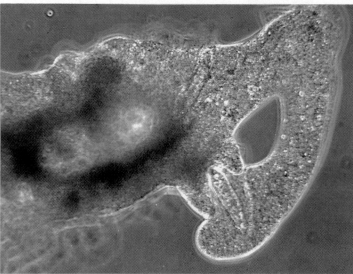

WITH WHICH TO ENGULF A PARAMECIUM. CHEMICAL STIMULI SOMEHOW ENABLE AMOEBAE TO DIFFERENTIATE BETWEEN EDIBLE AND INEDIBLE OBJECTS

DRAWN BY INVISIBLE HEAT WAVES, a white-lined sphinx moth assumes a mating posture on a warm infra-red transmitter. Philip S. Callahan, the American who set up this experiment, believes that certain night-flying moths use heat—i.e., infra-red—to find each other and the plants on which they feed and lay eggs. Thus a male could navigate towards a female whose temperature had been raised during flight. His night-adapted eyes would enable him to "see" her at a distance, and eyes and antennae working together might even help him to tell her species, as determined by a specific wing beat.

CRAWLING OVER A LOUDSPEAKER, female grasshoppers seem to be trying to get at the sound that has drawn them across hot sand. Both audible and ultrasonic frequencies affected them.

The Staccato Song of Love

Another sign stimulus, of course, is sound. A male bird's song attracts females and repels competitors. Thus, it acts as a signal to birds of the same species. So, too, does the strident song of the French grasshopper *Ephippiger bitterensis*. Through countless springs along the Mediterranean coast the males have been calling to the females with the stridulating organs they bear on their backs (*left*), and season after season the females have been scrambling towards them, crawling over obstacles that stand in the way, speeding up as they come closer and closer to their mates. But several years ago the males in the dunes near Montpellier received some strange competition. In many cases the females ignored them to go scurrying towards beeping loudspeakers, tweeting whistles and a variety of other noise makers. This was part of an experiment being performed by a group of French scientists, who analysed *Ephippiger bitterensis'* song and matched it with equipment they had brought with them.

They found that the females would respond to almost any sharp sound, even hand clapping. Mimicking the song was not important. What mattered was sharpness—and the quickness with which the sound was interrupted and resumed. Oddly, females failed to react to the artificial stimulus until the sound exceeded that of the male's by 15 to 25 decibels.

THE SOURCE OF THE MALE'S SONG is an organ on its back (*top*). Modified wings scrape against each other (*bottom*) to produce sound amplified and directed by the parabolic shell.

ACTING THE PIED PIPER, a French scientist demonstrates how a female grasshopper can be attracted to his hand—and eventually to his lips—by repeated blasts of a Galton whistle.

Displayed on the cage are other pieces of equipment used to test the responses of grasshoppers to sound. Labelled to indicate frequencies, they range from bird callers to police whistles.

DECOY EGGS tried out on herring-gulls include specimens made from wood and glass in a variety of shapes. Some bear markings ranging from pallid spots to bold polka dots.

Egg and Superegg

Like the female grasshoppers, herring-gulls will also respond to an artificial stimulus of a supernormal kind, with extremely interesting and sometimes amusing results. Presented with a wooden egg many times larger than its regular product, a brooding herring-gull will actually prefer the larger egg (*below*). Why this should be so is not yet fully understood. What is known is that several stimuli, rather than one, come into play here—colour, markings, shape and size all working together to signify *egg*

IN ITS NEST ON A NORTH SEA ISLAND, A HERRING-GULL INSPECTS TWO PAINTED WOODEN EGGS, ONE NORMAL SIZE, THE OTHER 20 TIMES AS

to the gull and release the appropriate behaviour in the bird. To measure the relative value of such stimuli in egg recognition, Dutch scientists devised an ingenious experiment based on the tendency of the brooding gull to retrieve an egg that has rolled or been accidentally kicked from the shallow nest. In the bird's absence, the scientists removed the gull's eggs and substituted specimens from the collection at the left. They placed them, generally two at a time, at the rim of the nest rather than inside—

thereby encouraging the gull upon its return to choose between the artificial eggs and reveal a preference. All sorts of egg substitutes were tried in all sorts of combinations.

The tallied responses showed that the birds preferred speckled eggs to plain ones, rounded eggs to sharp-edged ones, and large eggs to small ones—the larger the better. But, of all these varied visual stimuli, two seemed to play a more important role in egg recognition than the others: shape and size.

LARGE. IGNORING THE SMALL EGG, IT TRIES TO INCUBATE THE GIANT, CONTINUING ITS FRANTIC EFFORTS ALTHOUGH IT KEEPS TOPPLING OFF

The Odd Results of Inner Conflicts

What happens when stimuli work against each other, rather than together? As might be expected, the animal develops a conflict, the resolution of which may at first seem completely inappropriate to the situation. The male stickleback, for example, will attack another male venturing into its territory, but if both meet at the common boundary of their territories, they will be motivated both to fight *and* to flee. Since these drives are antagonistic, the males may begin to dig pits, an activity associated with nesting but here appearing as a result of their emotional conflict.

Similarly, the female oyster-catcher seeing itself in a mirror (*opposite*) is stimulated to fight, only to find that its "adversary" will not flee. As a result, the female's own drive to retreat comes into play. Reflecting this conflict, the bird stands still and adopts a sleeping posture.

BRISTLING ALL OVER, a male Japanese egret reacts to the presence of a female in its territory with a threat display. If the pair are to mate, however, the female must quietly persist in coming back until allowed by the male to remain at the edge of the territory. Only then can active courtship proceed.

CONFRONTED BY ITS REFLECTION IN A MIRROR, A FEMALE OYSTER-CATCHER IS IMMEDIATELY ROUSED TO ATTACK THE "INTRUDER" (BELOW)

ITS REPEATED BLOWS UNAVAILING, THE FEMALE FINALLY TUCKS ITS BEAK INTO ITS SHOULDER FEATHERS BUT KEEPS BOTH EYES OPEN

A BROODY HEN, deprived of chicks, takes two orphaned kittens under its wing. In turn, the kittens seemed unperturbed by its attentions and played about with the old hen as though it were a cat—and even licked its feathers. But then the kittens began to find their foster mother less and less satisfactory, and finally they abandoned the hen, to grow up into cats.

FEEDING PET GOLDFISH, which surfaced in the hope of titbits, a cardinal pops an insect into a gaping mouth. It did this for several weeks, perhaps because its nest had been destroyed.

Mistaken Identities

Since most animals respond to but a few of many possible stimuli in any given situation, they may on occasion be misled into inappropriate behaviour by seemingly appropriate stimuli. Such behaviour is known as misfiring. The classic example of this is provided by the European song-bird that not only hatches the oversize egg laid in its nest by the cuckoo but rears the oversize fledgling, even though the interloper pushed the bird's own eggs or young out of the nest. Despite the loss of its brood, the parent's dominant instinct is still to feed young. Thus, like the cardinal shown at the left, when it sees the sign stimulus of a wide open mouth, it does what that stimulus commands—it stuffs insects down inside.

FONDLING PETS, THIS LITTLE GIRL MAY BE SAID TO EXHIBIT A MISFIRING OF HER MATERNAL INSTINCT

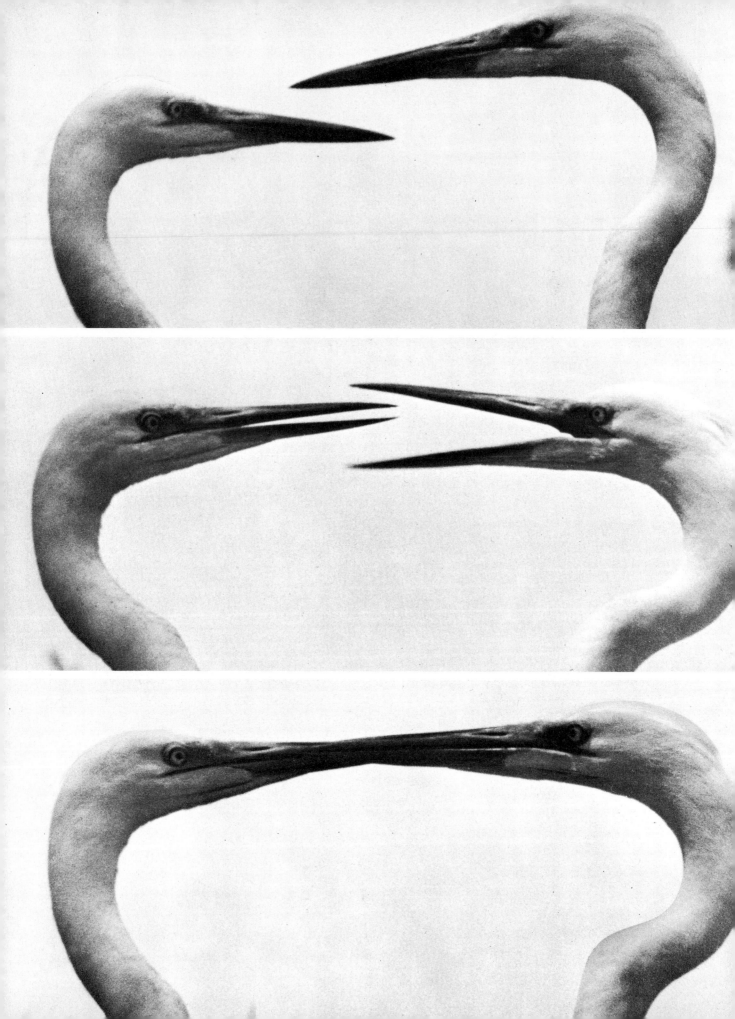

4

The Machinery of Behaviour

THE amazing perceptual abilities of animals make it tempting to believe that if only we knew enough about their response to outside stimuli we could prove that their behaviour is controlled entirely by them—that animals are in fact mere "reflex automata", slaves, albeit complicated ones, of the outside world. And this indeed is what some biologists have claimed in the past.

However, we know now that things are not that simple, and that an animal's behaviour must be controlled from within as well as from the outside. One everyday fact alone makes that obvious: a satiated animal will usually refuse even the most tempting food. This is illustrative of a very general phenomenon. When we observe an animal's behaviour at different times in the same environment, we find that it responds in all gradations of behaviour from a full response to none at all. Conversely, if we compare repeated responses of animals to natural stimuli on various occasions, we find that it sometimes requires very strong stimulation to elicit a reaction, while at other times an animal responds to only the slightest stimulus.

Sometimes animals may even exhibit behaviour without any of the stimuli normally associated with such acts. Flies will always preen their wings as soon as dust particles stick to them—but why do flies without wings, even aberrant mutants that have never grown any wings at all, make these wing-cleaning movements regularly, so to speak *in vacuo*?

This type of behaviour may seem entirely spontaneous, since we cannot observe any visible, external stimulus which could cause the fly to clean the wings it does not have. But this conclusion, like any others based on such observations, has a flaw. It argues by elimination, saying that as long as no reason for an act of behaviour can be detected it must be spontaneous. If we are to really prove that internal factors have caused the animal to show this "vacuum behaviour", we must attack such internal factors directly. This brings us deep into the study of the animal's physiological make-up.

Among the best-known internal agents are the hormones. These chemical messenger substances are released into the blood by the endocrine glands, and they not only stimulate certain growth processes but also influence many behaviour patterns. For instance, the sex glands of vertebrates produce sex hormones which are necessary—though not in themselves sufficient—to make an animal show its full sexual behaviour. Lacking sex hormones, castrated cocks neither crow nor mate, nor do castrated male sticklebacks build nests. But when such castrated animals are injected with the male sex hormone, they will again act sexually like normal males.

So far-reaching are the effects of hormones that their study has grown into a separate science, endocrinology. It is now known, for instance, that reproductive behaviour is controlled by a variety of hormones, some of which are secreted by the sex glands, and others by a tiny gland near the brain, the pituitary. Some of these pituitary hormones stimulate the sex glands to produce their sex hormones in the first place, and the two together have a great variety of effects. Full sexual behaviour in most cases, including courtship display, fighting and guarding the nest, will occur in most animals only when both pituitary and sex hormones are supplied in the correct sequence.

OTHER internal stimuli are provided by sense receptors. Mammals urinate when sense receptors in the wall of the bladder respond to increasing tension as the bladder fills up. Similarly, breathing quickens when the respiratory centres in the hindmost part of the brain signal an overabundance of carbon dioxide in the blood. Many other such internal sense receptors perform functions directly related to behaviour.

But are such agents as hormones and internal sensory stimuli the only sources of spontaneity of behaviour? Does the central nervous system always require specific stimulation, albeit from somewhere else within the body, in order to cause behaviour to occur? Or can it fire on its own initiative? These questions are more easily asked than answered. It is true that isolated bits of central nervous tissue have been observed under certain circumstances to fire rhythmically in much the same way as they fire normally in the intact body, and this lends support to the notion, now gaining acceptance, that the nervous system is more than a mere reflex machine. It is quite possible, and even likely, that many parts of the nervous system normally have a certain "rest output". But this, of course, does not mean that this spontaneous nervous activity is entirely independent of conditions outside the nervous system—a normal blood and oxygen supply, for instance, is indispensable.

Such rhythmic firing of isolated bits of nervous tissue is a long way from a fly preening imaginary wings, and even further from a cat, which, though well fed, may set out to hunt. It is in practice extremely difficult to find out whether and how spontaneous nervous rhythms contribute to complex behaviour, but there are various indications that the nervous system, far from being passive and just waiting for specific commands, has a say in deciding whether or not it shall await such stimulation or dictate behaviour of its own accord.

When we speak of internal control of behaviour we must remember that we are thinking exclusively of the events immediately preceding the behaviour. These, however, are often themselves controlled by the environment. The hormones secreted by the pituitary and the sex glands are true internal determinants of reproductive behaviour, yet their secretion is itself at least in part controlled by external events—for instance, by the time of year. Many vertebrates of the northern Temperate Zone, if kept artificially under the light conditions of a typical short winter day, will not show the normal spring activity of these glands even though the season may be far advanced. But when the same animals are subjected to a régime of increasing day length or kept in a constant "day" of 16 hours' illumination and 8 hours' darkness, their pituitaries and sex organs will begin to secrete hormones and they may even reproduce in midwinter.

THE effect of such hormones on behaviour is not simple. Pigeons offer a case in point. They feed their young by regurgitating "crop milk", a substance rich in proteins secreted by glands in the crop. These glands are dormant in winter but become active when the pituitary begins to release the hormone prolactin. Because pigeons begin to feed their young when the prolactin content of the blood has become high, one might think that the prolactin controlled regurgitation directly. But in reality, prolactin only starts the process of regurgitation by making the crop tense with crop milk—regurgitation itself, the actual feeding process, requires the squab to press against the bird's breast. Winter birds will also regurgitate in response to a little outside pressure, provided their crops are really full, with milk or anything else, but they do not normally do so because they have no young to elicit regurgitation. Thus it is the presence of young and the tension in the crop together which effect parental feeding.

Behaviour, then, is controlled in an over-all way by external stimuli or the working of internal organs or—as is most generally the case—by a combination of both. But let us now have a look at the actual movements which the animal performs as the consequences of the various types of stimulation—at the actual behaviour patterns. Examined in detail, these reveal themselves as a marvellously complex sequence of large and small events. Reproductive behaviour of many birds, for example, begins with a male settling on a territory and driving off rivals, continues with a female joining him, progresses to copulation, nest building, incubation of the eggs and finally rearing of the young. All this is initiated by the lengthening daylight, which stimulates the pituitary gland; but this reaction of the pituitary is only the first step in the whole long series of reproductive phases. To understand the full sequence, we must obviously know more than just what set it off—we also need to know how the bird is made to switch into the right phase at the right time as the cycle of behaviour progresses.

Let us see how this works in one part of the reproductive sequence, nest building. Female canaries, like many other song-birds, build their nests in two phases. The main cup is built first, of grass and the like, and then it is lined with feathers. As the building progresses, it will be seen that the birds gradually collect less grass and more feathers. Now, we know that the building behaviour as a whole is under the control of hormones, because birds can be made to build out of season by injections of the female sex hormone, oestrogen. The switch from grass to feathers, however, is not due directly to hormone action, but to external stimuli: in plain language, when the female sits in the nest between bouts of collecting, she gets scratched by the grass.

Ordinarily the female would not be so sensitive to the texture of the nest, but as egg-laying time nears she begins to lose feathers from her underside, resulting in the creation of a bare piece of skin known as the brood patch. This well-timed loss of feathers is caused by hormone action which, in turn, is sparked by the presence of the male canary and the building of the nest cup. All these factors combine to produce the brood patch, which then begins to receive an increased blood supply so that the female will be able to warm her eggs as she sits on them. This also makes the brood patch increasingly sensitive to the touch. In this way the *effective* stimulation received from the nest becomes stronger, and this stronger stimulus somehow makes the female switch to collecting feathers. By lining the cup with this soft material the bird of course reduces the stimulus to a lower level.

This is only one of the many processes which control the orderly performance of reproductive behaviour. The entire machinery is beautifully integrated: hormone secretion and external stimuli interact continuously and in such a way that at each step the required behaviour is produced. Long series of experiments are needed to unravel all these interactions, and the full story is only gradually being worked out.

BUT even the phases themselves are complex sequences of behaviour in their own right. Each phase is built up of various cyclical patterns: a nest-building bird sets out to search for nest material, finds it, picks it up, tests it perhaps, and either rejects or accepts it. Then it flies to the nest, deposits it there and works it into the existing structure with various movements, such as pushing it into the nest's rim, sitting down in the nest and trampling with its feet so as to mould the nest cup. When this is done, it begins the cycle anew, setting out once more to collect the next bit of material.

Much of the natural behaviour of animals consists of such cycles, which are really recurrent series of relatively simple acts. We know in several cases how such so-called "action chains" are controlled. The first stage is usually spontaneous—i.e., internal changes cause a hungry animal to set out to search for food without having yet perceived any food. It is also highly variable, both in form and in duration, and goes on until food is perceived.

While this introductory searching phase, often called "appetitive behaviour", is controlled from within, the switch from this to the next act, and to those following, is often caused by specific external stimuli. The female digger-wasp, with which I conducted the experiments in shape recognition detailed in the previous chapter, has also given me some excellent illustrations of this. When this wasp goes out hunting for a prey animal to store in its burrow, it begins by flying to a heath or similar place where honey-bees are foraging on flowers. Bees are preferred prey (which is why this insect is also known as the bee-wolf), and the wasp will fly irregularly from plant to plant until it spots one. Once it sees a bee, the wasp flies straight at it and takes up a position three or four inches down wind from it. This is a visually controlled response—in fact, the entire hunt so far has been visually controlled—but the bee is apparently not yet recognized as a bee: a fly or even a chip of wood dangling in a spider's nest will make the wasp fly towards it and take up its position.

Now, however, we enter a new phase of the cycle. The wasp hovers in position for a few seconds—and then suddenly leaps at her prey. This leap is elicited by the scent of the bee—it is a chemical response which serves to identify the bee exactly for what it is. If the wasp has been attracted by another insect or even by a simple, visual but odourless dummy, she will not leap, but after a few seconds' hovering will abandon the false prey. If we have given the dummy a bee's scent by rubbing it against a real honey-bee, the wasp will leap and seize it. She will also leap at dead bees dangled in front of her, but she will not leap at a bee which has been de-scented by dipping it in ether.

The leap is normally followed by the wasp rapidly turning the bee round so that she faces it, whereupon she stings it under the chin, killing it. This next act is again elicited by special stimuli, in this case a matter of touch. The dummy must not merely look like a bee and smell like a bee but it must also *feel* more or less like a bee. A scented stick will not be stung, but a dead fly that has been given bee scent will be.

At each of these switches from one act to the next, the animal responds to specific stimuli—but it is notable that even when these emanate from the same object throughout, the animal at each stage selects certain sign stimuli and ignores others. It is clear therefore that the "centrifugal setting" or "gating" of the mechanisms responsible for the selection of the sensory input, which I discussed in Chapter 3, changes from moment to moment as an animal goes through such an action chain.

By this time, we have gone quite far in our dissection and analysis of behavioural activities—all the way down to the point where we begin to consider individual phases of movement, like walking, swimming and flying. But these, too, are sequences of events which must be pulled apart and analysed. What makes an animal move its feet in a regular rhythm to carry it over the ground? What makes a fish's fin sweep to and fro in a regular right-left sequence? How is the up-and-down alternation of a bird's wing controlled?

Actually, these sequences, too, are often under combined external and internal control. Of this the crawling of an earth-worm is a good example.

An earth-worm is built up of a number of segments. When the animal crawls, these segments are shortened and stretched in a regular alternating pattern, but there is a phase difference between successive segments, so that contraction waves are seen to travel from the front to the back of the animal. Contraction results in forward movement because each segment has backward-pointing bristles which prevent sliding back. It was shown long ago that when one cuts an earth-worm in two halves, the front end will crawl on, while the tail end will merely wriggle. But when one connects the last segment of the front part by a thread with the first segment of the rear part, the rear half will begin to crawl normally as soon as the thread has been pulled tight and so stretches the first segment. From this it was concluded that normal crawling was caused by the mechanical stretching effect which the contraction of each segment had on its back neighbour.

However, we know now that the contraction commands will also travel from front to rear if all segments have their sensory nerves cut so that the central nervous system cannot receive information from the stretched segments. The regular succession of contractions is therefore controlled in two ways; the behaviour is safeguarded by the joint action of two control mechanisms. In a similar, although not quite identical way, the undulatory swimming move-

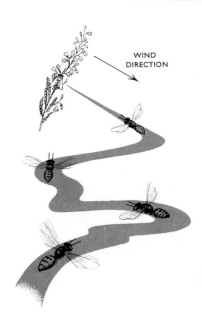

WIND DIRECTION

THE COMPLEX TASK OF KILLING A BEE

How a whole sequence of appropriate acts is regulated by outside stimuli is shown by the bee-hunting techniques of the digger-wasp. This wasp cruises about in a zigzag fashion until she spots what looks like a bee on a flower. However, her eyes alone are not sufficient to identify it positively as a bee, and so the wasp's next move is to station herself a few inches down wind and pause there for an instant while another sense comes into play. Now, if it smells like a bee, she darts in and grapples with it. If it also feels like a bee, she will try to turn it around facing her and sting it under the "chin". The whole operation can be summarized: sees bee, grabs bee, kills bee—each act triggered by a different stimulus.

IN DIFFICULT SITUATIONS
BIRDS AND MEN ACT ALIKE

Birds and men—and many other animals as well—experience the same emotional conflicts when they are urged ahead by anger but at the same time held back by fear or other emotions. Interestingly, the behaviour that comes out of this is markedly similar. Three ways that birds deal with this conflict are shown below, with the corresponding human actions shown on the opposite page.

DISPLACEMENT
ACTIVITY

MOSAIC
MOVEMENT

REDIRECTED
RESPONSE

Displacement activity is conflict that is expressed in an irrelevant manner. The starling at the top, facing a rival, will preen its feathers instead of the more logical act of fighting or pecking. In mosaic movement an animal attempts several acts but is inhibited from completing any of them. Here (centre) an angry gull stands with head down, ready to peck, and with wing ready to strike, but is frozen in this attitude. In redirected response an animal aims its feelings at a substitute object. Here a blackbird pecks furiously at a leaf instead of another bird.

ments of the tail of a fish are controlled partly by internal nervous activity, partly by reflex chains. Here the movements that alternate are contraction waves along the right and left sides of the body.

The individual acts of a chain, once elicited, can often run their full course without outside control. An animal that starts to run, triggered by an escape stimulus, can continue running in the absence of further stimulation, and even considerably more complicated behaviour acts may be carried to their conclusion, as it were, automatically. When the grayling butterfly, for example, has found a willing female, it starts an elaborate courtship ritual. This ends with an elegant bow: the male spreads its wings, moves them far forward and then, catching the female's antennae between them, presses them slowly together. This movement brings the male's scent-producing organs, which lie on the upper surface of its forewings, in contact with the female's organs of smell located on the antennae, and the resulting chemical stimulus elicits her mating behaviour. But the male will court a dead female, too—and not only that, but if the male has once started his bow, the female can be removed and he will go right on through the entire cycle. Only when he has completed his bowing activity will he start searching about for the now-absent female.

So far, we have been considering only what makes an animal *start* behaving: the circumstances, internal and external, that initiate a new movement. But for a full understanding of the machinery of behaviour it is also necessary to understand what makes an animal stop. Although it may not be obvious at first glance, one of the striking things about living creatures is that they not only do what is required of them; they do no *more* than is required. Unlike most machines, they do not have to be switched on and off by an outside manipulator; something is built into them that does this at the proper time.

What is the nature of this mechanism? Of course, in some cases an outside agent stops behaviour simply by providing a strong stimulus that triggers some quite different behaviour—as the appearance of a predator will make most animals stop feeding and start fleeing or crouching instead. Usually, however, an animal stops feeding of its own accord. Life processes are self-regulating; the animal oscillates around what is basically a steady state, doing neither too much nor too little. We have learned from electronics engineers that such a state can be maintained only if processes stop themselves when they are no longer required. This is done by "negative feedback"—an arrangement whereby the consequences of a process reduce it and, if necessary, bring it to an end.

A familiar example of negative feedback is furnished by the oil burner and thermostat that regulate the temperature in a house. The burner has only two modes of operation—on and off. When the burner is on, the room warms up until a preset temperature is reached at which point the thermostat cuts off the electricity so that the burner stops. In other words, the consequences of the burner's "on" mode turn it off. When the room has cooled to a certain point, the thermostat turns the burner on, and so it alternates between on and off, keeping the room temperature fluctuating around an average value determined by the setting of the thermostat.

Essentially, therefore, negative feedback involves the continuous correction of errors or deviations. The "machine" involved in the behaviour of animals, of course, is much more sophisticated than the oil-burner/thermostat combination, but the principle is the same, and our task, as behaviour students, is to find out just how this behaviour machinery prevents an animal from "overdoing it".

A relatively simple example is the feeding behaviour of most mammals. There are many possible consequences of eating that could tell an animal when it has had enough, but more than anything else it is the filling of the stomach that stops the feeding process. This was found out in a series of experiments with rats. A tube was inserted in the oesophagus of a group of test animals in such a way that food could be siphoned off as fast as it was eaten, before it reached the stomach; or, conversely, food could be put into the stomach through the tube without its being ingested in normal fashion through the mouth.

As always in such tests, a group of normal rats was used as a control—these were given specific amounts of food which they ate in the regular way. The test animals, meanwhile, were given the same amounts of food, except that in one group the meals never reached the stomach—they were drawn off through the tubes, while others were fed by pushing food directly into their stomachs without their going through the motions of eating it. In each case the rats were offered food a short time later, and the degree of satiation was judged from the amount that they would eat. Not surprisingly, it was found that the animals which had eaten without having filled their stomachs were prepared at once to eat normally, whereas both the normal animals and those whose stomachs had been filled from the outside showed every sign of being satiated. This was true even when the stomach was filled with non-nutritive bulk which could not be absorbed. We must therefore conclude that the presence of substance in the stomach produces a stimulus which removes the urge to feed.

So far, we have been analysing one behaviour at a time, and from scattered fragments of knowledge we have tried to piece together a picture of the combined internal and external control of such complex patterns as feeding or reproductive behaviour. But we have not yet considered how it happens that as a rule an animal does one thing at a time. It is imperative, of course, that it should attend to only one thing at a time, or nothing would get done; but with so very many behaviour patterns at its disposal, how does it manage to use only one at a time?

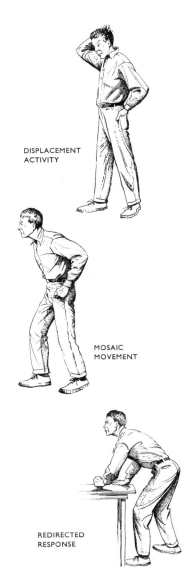

DISPLACEMENT ACTIVITY

MOSAIC MOVEMENT

REDIRECTED RESPONSE

Among humans similar expressions of inner conflict are common—and easily recognized. As an example of displacement activity, an angry man, unable to express his feelings directly, scratches his head in frustration. He may also make mosaic movements, clenching his fists and taking a threatening step forward, but remain frozen in this hostile stance, unable to complete his acts. In redirected response he may take out his feelings on a substitute target, a table, which he bangs with his fist—actually as appropriate as the blackbird's leaf pecking.

MIXED behaviour in most cases would be physically impossible; an animal cannot approach and evade the same object at the same time. On the other hand, a feeding antelope, startled by the scent of a lion, could theoretically try to snatch foliage off the bushes as it dashes away from the danger spot—yet it does not. Why? This is clearly a case of internal control, for however hungry the antelope is, and however tempting the food may be, it stops responding to these normally powerful stimuli and flees. How these different major behaviour patterns suppress others is practically unknown. A beginning of an analysis has been made in some simple cases, and there are indications that strong stimulation of one behaviour system inhibits, through connections within the central nervous system, all other behaviour systems, but the mechanics of this, or the circuitry involved, remain to be discovered.

There are numerous occasions, however, on which an animal is strongly stimulated in various ways at once, and when neither of the two or even three behaviour patterns involved wins out over the others. In such cases we observe "conflict behaviour". Many threat displays observed when male birds intimidate their rivals are examples of such conflict behaviour. The male is at the same time stimulated to attack and to flee—it is aggressive as well as afraid. It displays this behaviour most often right on the boundary of its territory, just where fear of the opponent prevents a further advance. In geese the threat postures have been produced experimentally by presenting two sets of stimuli together:

those which normally make the geese flee, and those which make them attack.

These and other conflict movements are of great interest because they are often "understood" by other individuals—they act as signals and so form the basis of animal "language". I shall discuss in Chapter 7 how such signals work.

We have come a long way since we began to ask simply why an animal behaves the way it does. We have seen that behaviour is controlled in a great variety of ways from the outside and from within. Outside stimuli are selectively admitted, dependent on the internal condition of the animal. The sensory data are processed and integrated in complicated ways. Movements are produced by beautifully co-ordinated muscle contractions. The internal state of the animal changes from month to month, from hour to hour, from second to second. With each change the animal is not only made to perform different movements but also to "open the gate" selectively to special stimuli. Different parts of the behaviour machinery keep each other in check and struggle for dominance. Whatever an animal does, its machinery is such that at the crucial points "negative feedback" prevents it from overdoing it.

Our knowledge of all these intricate processes is still extremely slight. The machinery is being studied in a variety of ways. On the one hand, the behaviour of the intact animal is analysed by psychologists and ethologists, and this analysis reveals to us step by step what kinds of things the as-yet-unknown machinery must do so that the animal can behave properly. On the other hand, the machinery is also being investigated in the laboratory: the processes in nerve cells and in centres and circuits are being studied by physiologists, and attempts are made to see how these processes, combined and integrated, could possibly produce the behaviour we see the intact animal perform. As yet the two fields of research have not really made contact. The processes in single nerve cells are found to be much more complicated than was believed even 20 years ago, and a major effort of many physiologists goes into the analysis of these processes. Prominent physiologists feel increasingly uncertain whether they have discovered all the principles governing the co-ordination between nerve cells and groups of nerve cells which result in behaviour. Students of the behaviour of intact animals are likewise beginning to realize that their studies have at best provided the merest sketch of the way behaviour is organized.

ONE could compare these positions of the physiologists and the behaviour students with two Martians studying the machinery which controls a car. One of them, an ethologist, sees cars run, accelerate, slow down or stop and follow bends in the road. He may have found out that a red light or absence of fuel brings the cars to a stop, and that turning the steering wheel makes the front wheels turn. But to find the connection between the pressing of the accelerator and increased speed, he will have to take the car apart. The other Martian, a physiologist, may understand in great detail the mechanics of the throttle or the way the air-gas mixture is controlled in the carburettor. But if neither he nor the ethologist has got any further, they will not be able to integrate their knowledge into a full understanding of the way a car works. We are at present very much in the position of these two Martians, the only difference being that the living body is infinitely more complex than a car. And when using this analogy we must not of course forget that the car functions properly only with an able driver inside. The behaviour machinery of a living animal can only be compared with the performance of car and driver combined, and it is the driver's responses that would offer the stiffest problems to the Martians.

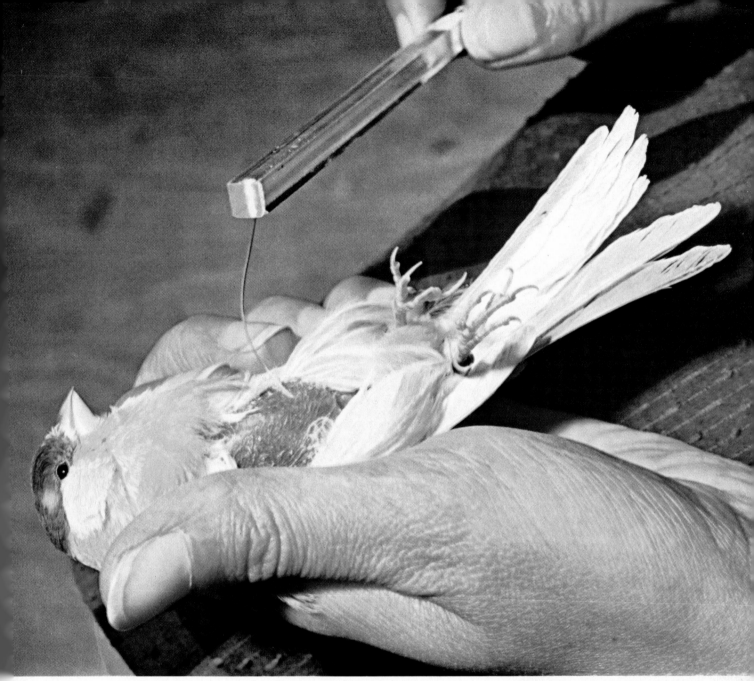

BRITISH ETHOLOGIST R. A. HINDE TESTS A CANARY'S BROOD PATCH. SECONDARY HORMONES MAKE IT MORE SENSITIVE AS NESTING TIME NEARS

A Labyrinth of Stimuli

An animal's behaviour is not determined simply by outside forces; in recent years science has become acutely aware of the interplay between external and internal stimuli. To unravel this complex tangle of forces, behaviourists have moved into the laboratory, where they tamper with the very machinery of behaviour, seeking the physical fountain-heads of an animal's ever-changing actions.

1 As the days lengthen in the springtime, the warm sun (arrows) activates the canaries' sex glands, stimulating the production of primary hormones (small symbols): androgen in the male and oestrogen in the female. This is the first step in a long chain of events that will ultimately result in egg laying and rearing of young.

The Forces that Control Mating in Canaries

In order to reproduce successfully, a canary must find a mate, build a nest, lay her eggs, incubate them, and feed the young. This involves a number of physiological and behavioural changes, each of which must occur at the right time and in the right order. Some of these are the result of external stimuli, such as sunlight or the presence of the male. Others come from within the female herself. These changes have been studied in detail by the British behaviourist R. A. Hinde, who has been working for years to unravel the complete cycle of canary reproduction and who has succeeded in pin-pointing the sources of several important stimuli that affect the female's bodily functions and behaviour. For the sake of clarity, the various phases in the courtship and nesting cycle are shown in this diagram as separate steps. Actually, reproductive development is a continuous, flowing process—with some of the forces that act on the birds steadily increasing while others are dwindling.

2 The production of androgen in the male's testes begins to have a noticeable influence on his courtship behaviour; he sings and displays, further stimulating the production of oestrogen in his mate. The arrow in this picture (*above*) indicates the principal source of external stimulation affecting the female's behaviour.

3 As a result of the continued stimulation by the presence of the male, the female starts collecting the material that she will use in the construction of her nest. At about this same time the tiny eggs that have been developing in her ovaries begin a rapid increase in size; at this stage they are about the size of seed pearls.

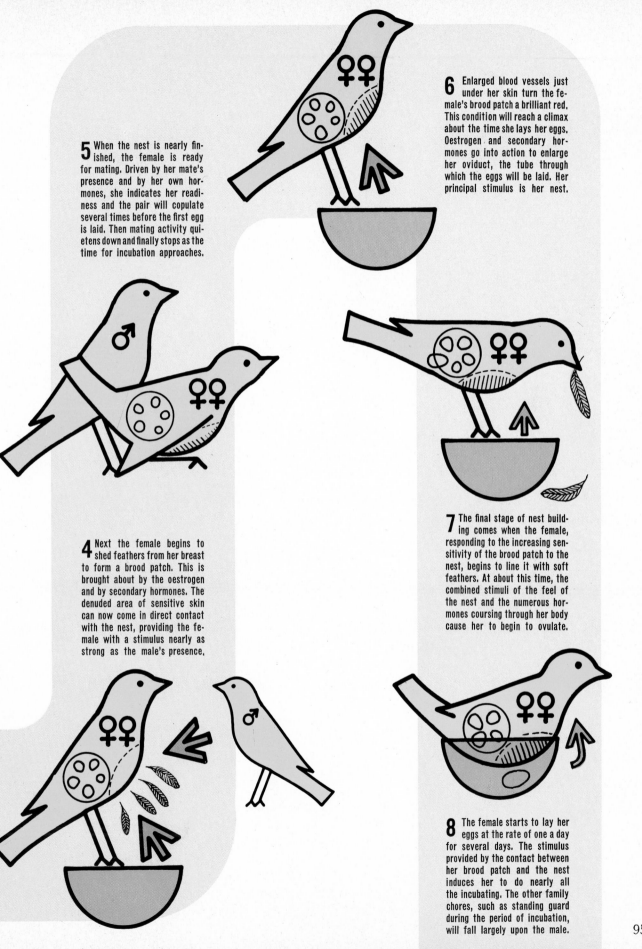

5 When the nest is nearly finished, the female is ready for mating. Driven by her mate's presence and by her own hormones, she indicates her readiness and the pair will copulate several times before the first egg is laid. Then mating activity quietens down and finally stops as the time for incubation approaches.

6 Enlarged blood vessels just under her skin turn the female's brood patch a brilliant red. This condition will reach a climax about the time she lays her eggs. Oestrogen and secondary hormones go into action to enlarge her oviduct, the tube through which the eggs will be laid. Her principal stimulus is her nest.

4 Next the female begins to shed feathers from her breast to form a brood patch. This is brought about by the oestrogen and by secondary hormones. The denuded area of sensitive skin can now come in direct contact with the nest, providing the female with a stimulus nearly as strong as the male's presence.

7 The final stage of nest building comes when the female, responding to the increasing sensitivity of the brood patch to the nest, begins to line it with soft feathers. At about this time, the combined stimuli of the feel of the nest and the numerous hormones coursing through her body cause her to begin to ovulate.

8 The female starts to lay her eggs at the rate of one a day for several days. The stimulus provided by the contact between her brood patch and the nest induces her to do nearly all the incubating. The other family chores, such as standing guard during the period of incubation, will fall largely upon the male.

PINE CHAFER BEETLES PREPARE TO MATE. THE ENTIRE ADULT LIFE OF THESE INSECTS—TWO TO THREE WEEKS—IS DEVOTED TO PROPAGATION

Getting the Sexes Together

Mating is, for all its apparent simplicity, as complicated a matter as it is fundamental to survival. First, it requires partners of the same species. They must both be fertile, and they must be fully prepared to copulate. To cope with these problems, virtually every species has varied and well-developed ways of getting the sexes together at mating time. These may include special sensory adaptations, flamboyant sexual displays or unique behavioural patterns. The male pine chafer beetle (*above*) is representative of many insects in that it seems to use antennae studded with olfactory receptors, in this case grouped in a bushy moustache, to locate and woo females. The Uganda kob (*opposite*), like many mammals, follows a distinctive ritual in which several stimuli—visual, tactile and olfactory—come into play.

96

MALE KOBS SPAR IN A TERRITORIAL DISPUTE. SUCH DISPLAYS, WHICH SELDOM END IN INJURY, DECIDE POSSESSION OF COURTSHIP ARENAS

PRANCING UP TO A FEMALE IN HIS TERRITORY, THE MALE THEN CARESSES HER (BELOW), TESTING WHETHER SHE WILL BE RECEPTIVE TO HIM

FEMALE OSTRICHES HIGH-STEP ON A KENYA SAVANNAH, TRYING TO ENTICE A NEARBY MALE. ALTHOUGH OSTRICHES ARE LUDICROUSLY UNGAINL

The Vamps of the Savannah

Only very rarely in the ritual of courtship does the female assume the dominant role and make the bulk of the sexual advances. An outstanding example of such aberrant behaviour is the mating dance of the ostrich, in which the males are the wooed rather than the wooers—and this despite the fact

A FEMALE, CONFIDENT OF HER SEDUCTIVENESS, LEAVES THE GROUP

OST OF THE TIME, THEIR COURTSHIP DANCE IS SURPRISINGLY GRACEFUL

THE MALE PURSUES HER IN A WILD CHASE THAT WILL END IN MATING

that they carry finer plumage, usually a sign of sexual aggressiveness. Most perplexing of all is that ostriches in captivity exhibit the normal standard of male dominance. Captive females make awkward attempts to mimic their mates; they also adopt traits detrimental to survival, such as laying their eggs in communal nests that no one bird could possibly incubate. Animal behaviourists are constantly being confronted with similar mysteries, illustrating the fact that although much has been observed about the actions of animals, a great deal has still to be learned about the mechanisms that control these actions.

WILD AND STRANGE are the mating antics of these Tibetan bar-headed geese high on a mountain lake. For unknown reasons, this spectacular wing-spreading ritual takes place after the birds have copulated in the water. Most commonly both birds spread their wings, although in this picture it is the male alone, rising breathtakingly behind his mate. Since the science of animal behaviour must exclude such subjective words as "joy" from its vocabulary, phenomena like this must await further research before they can be satisfactorily explained.

Stimulating Terror or Rage

GAS IS INHALED by a cat with no previous record of fear for mice; in fact, it had a healthy propensity for chasing them. How gas affects it is shown below. Effects last a few hours.

Just as in human psychology, abnormal behaviour in animals offers one of the most effective ways of understanding normal behaviour. In laboratories all over the world, scientists are subjecting animals to unnatural stimuli and carefully scrutinizing their reactions. One of the most dramatic of these behavioural experiments (*below and left*) shows a cat exhibiting a very uncatlike cowardice when confronted with a pair of harmless mice released in its cage. The source of this behaviour is a debilitating gas—its formula kept secret for obvious military reasons—that attacks the cat's nervous system and temporarily destroys the will to fight.

In another battery of experiments, Dr. Murray Glusman of the New York State Psychiatric Institute stimulates cats' brains directly by means of small electrodes implanted in the hypothalamus, a

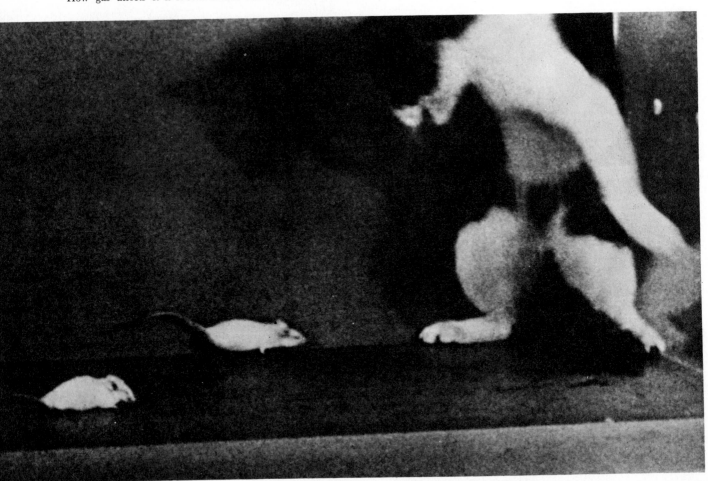

THE GASSED CAT, recoiling with fright at the sight of its former prey in its cage, retreats into a corner and squeals in terror. The experimenters do not know whether the cat saw the mice as deadly predators or whether the gas simply made its nerves so sensitive that it would flee from any motion. The mice, bewildered by such odd behaviour, ran around aimlessly.

portion of the brain known to be linked to emotions and thought to be linked with the processes of memory and learning. Sometimes the results are startling. When the brain of a cat that had been reared in close friendship with a rat was stimulated, it assaulted the rat brutally (*below and right*). Amazingly, the cat showed no sign a moment later of remembering its aggressive behaviour. Time after time it was made to attack the rat, but as soon as the artificial stimulation ceased, it was as friendly as ever. It may never be determined whether the stimuli produced a genuine rage that was immediately forgotten or whether the anger was an automatic reaction like that which makes a person kick when his knee is tapped. Recent experiments indicate that such rational functions as memory and learning may be entirely obscured during extreme emotion.

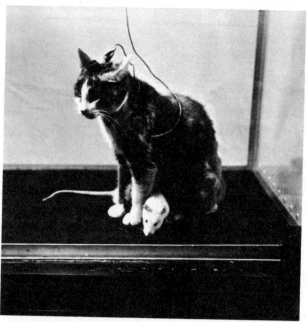

GOOD FRIENDS, a cat and a rat coexist comfortably in this quest into the origins of anger. Peace prevailed until a current was applied to the wires implanted in the cat's brain.

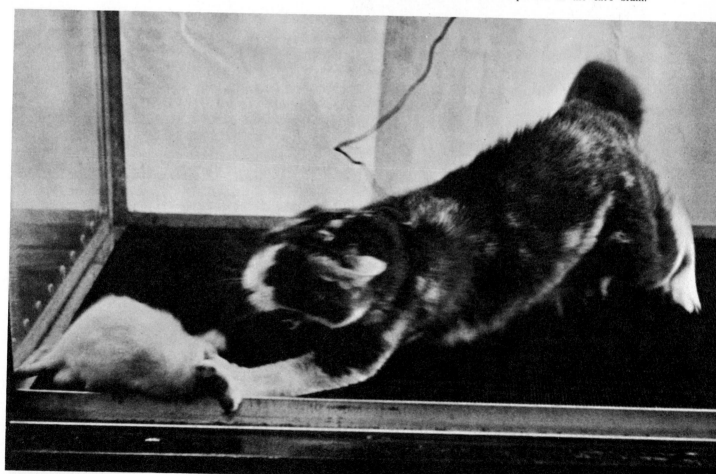

SUDDEN RAGE seizes the cat as electricity surges into its brain, making it attack its former friend viciously. Stronger current caused equally fervent flight. By shifting wires, Dr. Glusman found that the portion of the brain that controls the urge to flee is much larger than the part that causes a fight. After the test, the rat cautiously renewed the friendship.

103

The Revealing Webs

A striking example of artificially produced animal behaviour has come about as a by-product of drug research. Pharmacologist Peter Witt discovered that spiders spin strange, mis-shapen webs when they are under the influence of drugs. Each drug compels the spider to produce a different type of web, and in its behaviour the spider shows an eerie resemblance to disorientations experienced by human beings under the same drug. The graph-like webs can accurately identify the type of drug much more quickly than the usual lengthy laboratory analysis could.

DRUGGING A SPIDER, Witt squeezes a drop of fluid from a syringe, which the spider mistakes for a trapped insect. He can also dope a subject by tossing a drug-filled fly into the web.

A NORMAL WEB has the familiar spider architecture. The most efficient snare in nature, it has none the less many flaws.

PERVITIN, a benzedrine-like stimulant, makes the spider too impatient to circle the centre. It spins only in one small area.

CHLORAL HYDRATE, the barman's "Mickey Finn", puts the spider to sleep after it has completed only a small part of its web.

CAFFEINE produces the arachnid equivalent to human coffee nerves, making the spider spin a haphazard tangle of threads.

LYSERGIC ACID INDUCES ACUTE CONCENTRATION. THE SPIDER ZEALOUSLY WEAVES A PERFECT WEB, GREATLY IMPROVING ON NATUR

NAVIGATING BY SOUND, a bat
flies in pitch-darkness through a
maze, guided by the echoes of its
ultrasonic shrieks. It negotiated
this tangle of tubing for six hours
of tests without a single mishap.

5

Finding One's Way About

IF YOU should be caught in a sudden blizzard on the plains or a real cloud-burst in the forest, you might well decide that it was time to go home. How-ever, you might find that under such conditions of howling storm you would soon grow confused and lose your way. Such an experience points to the fact that it is not enough just to decide to head for home at an appropriate time and then start walking. No matter how good a walker you may be or how well your behaviour may be timed, you will not get home unless you are also able to orientate yourself in space.

This is a simple illustration of a basic rule that is true of all animals: to be effective, behaviour has to be controlled in space as well as time. Animals have to find their habitat, their food, a resting place, a mate, their nest and many other things; they have to move away from predators—in short, they must know where to go and where to be or, looking at it another way, where not to go or be. They also have to keep themselves properly positioned in space. We may take it for granted that we stay right side up, but even if we are not conscious of it, part of our behavioural machinery is constantly at work keeping us that way, and even some fishes, supported though they are on all sides by

ENGLAND IS "THATAWAY"

How do Baltic starlings know where England is? Obviously they do, for each year they migrate from an area east of the Baltic Sea to England and northern France, as shown by the tinted area in the map above. Experiments reveal that the navigating ability of starlings is of two kinds, innate and learned. Young birds have a natural tendency to fly in a south-westerly direction. When some were trapped at The Hague during migration and released again at Geneva, they continued on their south-westerly course and ended up in Spain. Older birds, who had made the trip before, realized they were off course and flew north-west from Geneva, as shown by the arrows below.

water, have to make an active effort to stay right side up in their medium. And while the approximate time at which a given behavioural pattern has to occur is often controlled from within, and although the moment is often determined with more precision by an internal stimulus, orientation, which controls where an animal shall be and go with respect to the outside world, depends on outside cues alone.

Many animals are capable of truly astonishing feats of orientation. The classic example is the migration of birds, and those species whose inexperienced young travel over tremendous distances all on their own have posed particularly difficult problems to science. How does a young wheatear, hatched in the summer in far northern Greenland, find its way through lonely nights of flying to countries thousands of miles to the south in western Africa? How do the petrels that breed on Tristan da Cunha and in the autumn swarm out over the vast Atlantic find their way back to their tiny island in the spring? Nor are these even the most spectacular of known migrations. The eels from the Atlantic seaboards of both North America and Europe travel in the darkness of the ocean depths to spawning grounds 200 fathoms down in the Sargasso Sea, and their offspring, little larval creatures, drift all the way back, each to its respective coast, and manage to find the fresh-water streams and lakes many miles inland that are their habitat. Salmon do the opposite, travelling back from the ocean to spawn in the particular river where they grew up years before.

THESE are peak achievements of orientation, but actually they differ only in degree from more everyday examples of animals finding their way about. Birds of prey will fly unerringly for miles to hunting grounds where they had success the day before. A sea-gull flying from its nest to its feeding ground follows a flight path that leads it from one updraught to another over the tops of the hills—and this path varies with the direction of the wind. And a fish, swimming in a dim world that to us seems to have no up or down at all, has none the less unmistakable information of where "up" is.

Orientation is an ever-present necessity; in fact, very few behaviour patterns are not orientated. And it is a very complex business indeed. Rarely, for instance, do fins, wings or legs on the right and left sides act with equal force: without guidance based on external stimuli, their movements would make animals move erratically or in circles. Thus a consistent course cannot be steered or a constant position maintained without continuous checking and correcting, just as a plane must be steered with constant corrections through vagrant wind currents when it comes in to land.

On some occasions, however, animals behave like a man firing a gun, checking—i.e., aiming—first and then "pulling the trigger" of their behavioural action. That is what the praying mantis and the chameleon do when they strike their prey. Similarly a lurking pike, when it sees a small fish approaching, positions itself precisely and then darts forward, with probably no chance to correct its forward rush once it has started.

In a few cases it has actually been demonstrated that a behaviour movement is controlled by two entirely different mechanisms that act simultaneously. Like a ship which is pushed through the water by its propeller and guided by its rudder, one mechanism dictates when a movement shall take place and with what force and for how long, while the other guides the direction of the movement in space. An example of this is the behaviour of ground-breeding birds when an egg accidentally rolls out of the nest.

Rectifying such an accident can clearly be a delicate problem, since an egg rolls so erratically even on smooth and level ground. What the bird does is quite wonderful to see. Sitting on the nest, it stretches its head forward until its bill reaches behind the egg, then, with constant tiny correcting movements to keep the egg rolling straight, it rolls it back into the nest again. Even gulls, whose bills are flattened sideways, manage to do this on very uneven terrain. If one substitutes a cylinder for the lost egg and provides a smoothly sloping platform, the bird will retrieve the cylinder in the same way—only now the retrieving movement will be a smooth sweep, since no corrective motions are needed. To use the ship analogy, only the propulsive force is needed; the guiding action is superfluous and so does not take place. Even more striking is what happens when the egg is removed just after the bird has started to retrieve it, as may be done with a tame goose—the goose goes right on making the retrieving movement just as though the egg were there, but it makes no other movements to steer the egg.

Young thrushes show the same thing in a different way. From the time they are hatched, they gape, opening their beaks wide, whenever the nest is slightly jarred, as it might be by the landing of a returning parent. They cannot see; their gaping is simply directed vertically upwards, steered by the gravity sense of the organ of the inner ear. When they are about a week old, their eyes open, and now their gaping can be elicited by visual stimuli, such as showing them models of the parent. But for a few days the gaping will still be aimed vertically upwards, even if the visual stimulus comes from one side: in this case, while the time of gaping is now controlled by the eye, the steering is still done by the gravity organs. Only after a few days do they direct their aiming visually, gaping at the parent's head where the food is.

A question that naturally arises when we undertake to study the orientation of an animal is what sense organ it uses. Clearly, not all sense organs are equally suitable to supply us with cues as to where things are—and thus where we are. Our nose may tell us that fresh bread is being baked in a shop somewhere near by, but we need our eyes to find it if we want to buy some. And this immediately indicates another important point: to be effective for purposes of orientation an organ must be able to "dissect" the sensory field—it must at least be sensitive to different degrees of stimulation from different directions, and preferably it should give information about the distances involved as well.

THIS kind of sensitivity requires an array of sensory cells, and usually some further apparatus accessory to the cells themselves, like the lenses we have in our eyes. Visual acuity has a direct relationship to visual information about direction: obviously, the sharper its vision, the better an animal can orientate itself by visual means. The same applies to hearing. Vertebrate ears, if used singly, are not very good at detecting the direction from which sounds come, but the two ears together give surprisingly accurate information. This is because the brain can detect minute time differences in the input from the two ears—a sound wave coming from the right reaches the right ear a tiny fraction of a second before it reaches the left, and this, combined with the fact that the left ear is in the "sound shadow" of the head, gives the brain a directional cue. If the sound is coming from straight ahead, we have to turn our head or use some other aid to tell for certain whether the source of the sound is in front of us or behind.

Sometimes two different sense organs, like those of smell and touch, may act together to give directional information. Scent, for instance, is carried by either

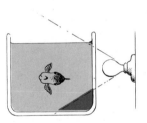

UP IS WHERE THE "SUN" IS

How does a fish know which way is up? By a combination of orientations to light and gravity. In a small aquarium with a bright light overhead, a fish will maintain a vertical position. If the light is put at one side, the fish will tilt a little, but not much, because its balancing organ— the otolith—is still making it react to gravity. But if the otolith is removed, the fish will flip over on its side (bottom picture) to keep the "sun" overhead.

air or water—many animals detecting a scent are able to follow it to its source (or, if it spells danger, go away from it) by reacting to the movements of the medium—wind, if the scent is carried by air, currents if it is borne by water. Many mammals even use three senses: their noses alert them to the scent, their senses of touch or temperature or perhaps both tell them the direction of the wind which carries the scent (as we might hold up a wet finger), and their eyes then guide their further movements. Many crabs, crayfish and shellfish, such as the whelk, will even create movements of the medium—they suck in water from one direction after another, thus scanning their surroundings chemically, and internal sense organs then tell them in what direction the sampling organ is pointing when the scent is strongest.

Such co-operation between senses, where each alone could not give sufficient or useful directional information, is responsible for spectacular achievements like the migrations of the eels. In the first long stage of their travels, the eel larvae, born in the Sargasso Sea, drift slowly with the currents towards their respective coasts in North America or Europe, growing as they go. But when they reach the shallow coastal waters, they begin to show a most remarkable and active behaviour. Whenever the ebb tide runs strongly away from the shore line, they rest on the bottom or in the sand, staying where they are. But when the flood tide begins to run in towards the coast, they swim up into the top layers, letting the current carry them towards shore, settling down again only when the tide turns. In this way they are carried by successive flood tides towards the brackish waters of the shore line and ultimately reach the estuaries of the rivers. Here they begin a new phase, reacting to the ebb tide by swimming actively against the current, and this carries them finally into the fresh water far up stream which they seem to detect by the characteristic odour of the dissolved substances it carries.

Thus the behaviour of these little eels, or elvers, involves a variety of responses: clinging to the bottom at one stage, swimming upwards at another, swimming against the current at yet another. Each has its own orientation mechanism; each reacts at a certain time to a certain condition; each is a relatively simple matter in itself—but all together they guide these seemingly uncomplicated creatures back to the habitat which their parents left months or years before they were born.

How do the mechanisms of orientation work? They all have one basic quality in common: however much they may differ in detail, and however different the problem of orientation may be for the animal concerned, two things are always involved. First the animal is informed that it has deviated from the required position; next it must act upon this information until a second sensory message tells it that the required position is regained.

What this means is that the second set of sensory messages provides negative feedback, stopping the movement when it has achieved its aim. A relatively simple situation is that of gravity response, as in a fish that it tilted from its normal position by a sudden current. The otolith in each of its inner ears rests on a pad of sensory hairs. In the normal, or horizontal, position the pressure it exerts upon the hairs is not felt as a stimulus, but as soon as the fish tilts, the otolith exerts a slightly sideways, shearing pressure which bends the hairs to one side—and when this occurs a stimulus is registered. This is because the firing rate of the sensory nerve which registers the stimulus changes—it increases as it tilts to one side, but decreases as it tilts to the other. The more the fish tilts,

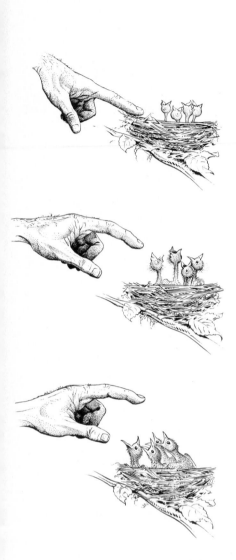

CHANGING STIMULI

Baby song-birds are born with the ability to stretch up their heads and gape for food when stimulated. At first they respond to any mechanical stimulus; a jarring of the nest by a human hand (top drawing) is as effective as that made by a parent bird alighting on the nest edge. Furthermore, being blind, their stretching can be guided only by gravity, and so they stick their heads straight up. A week later, with their eyes just opened (second drawing), they are now able to respond to the sight of an approaching hand, but they have not yet lost the gravitational control and still rear straight up. They lose this a few days later, and from then on a hand will not only elicit a response but will also orientate it (bottom).

the more the hairs are bent to that side—and the greater the change in the firing rate of the sensory nerve. And, as the fish brings itself back to normal, the bending of the hairs lessens, the firing of the nerve changes correspondingly, and in the horizontal position the normal firing rate is restored.

Thus the intensity of the stimulation that reaches the brain is, like the artificial horizon in an aeroplane, an accurate indicator of both the degree and the direction of tilting. In the brain the reports of the gravity organ in each ear are added to each other, which makes the instrument a very sensitive one indeed. A fish deprived of one of its gravity organs can still orientate itself, but not as promptly as with two.

As to the second phase of the operation, in which the quantity of stimulation is transformed into the nervous instructions which govern the movements of the fins and bring the fish upright, here we encounter not only a mechanism which we do not yet fully understand but a term that must be explained. The term is "target value". It means simply the desired situation, the aim of the animal. Thus, for a fish whose desire is to remain quietly right side up in the water, the target value is a moderate firing rate of the sensory nerve stimulated by the balancing mechanism in its ears. This is the only kind of stimulation that does not activate the fish to make corrective movements. It does nothing, and it stays where it is. If it were tipped in the water and its target value were still "right side up", then a change in the firing rate of the nerves would cause a slight correcting movement and restore the fish to an upright position. But how the changed firing rate is transmitted so that it results in the appropriate righting movement is not known.

As complicated as this relatively simple matter of staying right side up may seem to be, other orientation movements present an even greater challenge. Many involve a configurational stimulus—i.e., recognizing and acting upon shapes—and in many the shapes may even be in constant change. Our digger-wasp offers a good example as it returns to its burrow in the centre of a circle of pine cones. What is the image that presents itself as the wasp homes in on the burrow entrance? The entrance has a relationship to the circle—but as the wasp approaches, its position with respect to the circle is changing all the time, and therefore the image of the circle on the retina changes too. The wasp is therefore constantly orientating itself with respect to a changing image and decreasing distance, and yet somehow it manages to correct all deviations in response to these exceedingly complex stimuli and find its way home.

Considering this, we must assume that these stimuli caused by deviations from the desired course are translated or coded somewhere in the brain, like the varying bending or shearing qualities of the fish's otoliths, into graded intensities of stimulation. Too far to the right must result in a different degree of stimulation than not-so-far to the right or left or up or down.

Nor is this the whole story. When the digger-wasp has found its burrow and deposited its prey, it flies out to hunt more food. What does it orientate to now? If it were to base its outward flight on the same stimuli that guide it home, it would automatically return to the burrow as soon as it tried to leave. Quite different stimuli have to be involved to set it on its outward course, which means that the target values have to change, and this change must be governed by the internal state of the animal. This in turn means that the stimulation the animal "expects" when it moves about—i.e., the target value for which it is "set" in any given situation—can be changed by messages from inside the nervous

HOW A RAY BALANCES

The thornback ray is able to tell up from down by means of a set of otoliths, which are small pads of mucus-like material lying in cavities under the skin (arrow above). Each pad is weighted with heavy granules embedded in the mucus, and when the ray tilts to one side, this weight makes the pad slide one way or another in its cavity, bending some delicate hairs that it rests on. These hairs "fire", sending signals to the nerves at different rates, depending upon how they are bent (bottom).

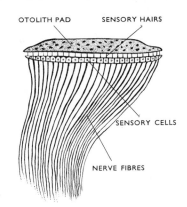

OTOLITH PAD   SENSORY HAIRS

SENSORY CELLS

NERVE FIBRES

Normal signal: hairs vertical

Slower signal: hairs bent to left

Faster signal: hairs bent to right

system: one set of values rules when the wasp is flying to the hunting grounds in search of prey, another when it has found and caught it. And this is actually the case, as we know from one of the most brilliantly simple experiments ever conceived and executed in this field.

The subject of the experiment was a fly, and the experiment itself depended on the fly's reaction to things moving in its surrounding environment. For an insect that is sitting still and desires to stay that way, the target value might be described as "no movement of the image on the retina"—in other words, no apparent motion of the objects around it. This is what the fly is "set" for, and therefore any movement of things around it will elicit a response. If the fly is resting inside a striped cylinder whose walls slowly begin to turn, the fly will turn too—just enough to keep the stripes where they "belong" and thus satisfy the requirement of "no movement on the retina". This response to movements of the surrounding environment is called the optomotor response.

THAT is all very well for a fly resting inside a turning cylinder, but what about a fly walking around in a cylinder that is not turning? How does it tell the difference between things that are themselves moving and things that only appear to move because the fly itself is in motion? The usual explanation offered—but never tested—was that the optomotor response was turned off by the fly when it wished to move itself. If it were left on, the reasoning went, the fly presumably would not be able to function, for as soon as it turned its head or walked a single step, the various objects around it would also seem to move, and the signal from its retina would instantly force it to stop in order to re-establish the target value of "no movement". Inasmuch as flies do walk about almost constantly, it was assumed that the optomotor response must somehow be disconnected when they wish to move.

The men who decided to test this were the German scientists Erich von Holst and Horst Mittelstaedt. With great ingenuity they took advantage of the fact that a fly has a very flexible "neck" and can turn its head almost completely around. So they simply twisted a fly's head through 180° and in this unnatural position glued it to the fly's body. Now the right eye was on the left, and the left on the right; this in turn meant that the image on the retinas would move in a direction opposite from the normal whenever the fly turned. Thus, when the fly began to walk and turn spontaneously, its eyes received a movement stimulus which ran in the opposite direction from the normal, providing positive instead of negative feedback.

The question was: how would the fly react to this reversed scheme of things? If the optomotor response, as had always been believed, was shut off when the fly began to walk and turn spontaneously, the reversed positions of the eyes should not really matter very much. But as the experimenters soon saw, the reversed eye positions mattered tremendously: as soon as the fly began to turn, it immediately got into a mad spin, turning faster and faster in the direction in which it started!

Only one conclusion was possible: the optomotor response was *not* cut off. Instead, a new target value was operating—not "no movement on the retina", which would simply have immobilized the fly, but one that might be labelled "movement at a certain speed and in a certain direction". It was this new target value which the experiment made so dramatically apparent. If the fly's eyes had been in the right position, it would have been able to function properly, but with their positions reversed, a left turn, for example, was interpreted as a right turn. Attempts to correct this only made the fly turn even farther to the left, or wrong, direction, with a mad spin the only possible result.

Thus it was proved that the brain does manage to "set" the data-processing visual centres in such a way that the target value changes continuously in precise correspondence to the movements an animal intends to make. A normal fly can turn whichever way it wants to; the target values change continuously with it, keeping the turn within the intended bounds. How this is done is a complete mystery still, but we do know that it *is* done.

A simple experiment anyone can perform will show this setting of the target value with respect to movement. If the environment around us moves, we respond to it—not by an optomotor response of moving with it, but simply by *seeing* it move. But if we turn our eyes from side to side deliberately, we do not have any sensation that the environment is moving, although we know that the image on our retina is moving. This poses the same problem as with the fly: does the target value change from "no movement" to "some movement"? Suppose now that we close one eye and press with a finger against the eyelid of the open one. This will cause the eyeball to move slightly—but passively, since its movement was induced by the finger and not by its own muscles. What happens? We see the room move.

Why don't we have this same sensation of seeing the room move when we move our eyes spontaneously? It must be because when we deliberately move our eyes, our brain is somehow told to *expect* movement—it is "set" for a counter-movement on the retina. The difference between moving an eye with its own muscles and pushing it around with a finger is that in one case the brain has sent out a command to the eye muscles and in the other it has not. The brain says "move", and so things are "set" to expect movement. The target value of the resulting visual stimulus changes when this command goes out, but only then. If we move the eye with our finger, no command is sent by the brain to the eye muscles through the usual nerve channels, no movement is expected, the target value does not change, and we see the room move.

Consider the reverse of this situation—suppose the command "move" is sent to the eyes, but the eyes do *not* move. This can be done by paralysing the eye muscles temporarily with an anaesthetic. In this case, everything else happens: movement is expected, a new target value is "set"—but the expected visual stimulus does not come because the eyes do not move. The surprising result is that the subject sees a movement of the environment when he tries to but cannot turn his eyes—he actually visualizes the target value directly.

FROM these experiments we get a glimpse of the incredibly complex and largely unknown processes that must go on in the brain during the behaviour sequences we have discussed in the previous chapter. Orientation guides almost every link in a behaviour chain. With every switch from one act to the next a new orientation mechanism is employed, or "set". When a bee flies from its hive to a flowering plant, it may first respond to a series of landmarks on the way from its hive to the plant. When it comes within sight of the plant, it responds to a rough outline of its shape, as we know because we can mislead it by putting up green dummies of roughly the same shape. When it comes nearer, it begins to orientate to the coloured flowers; when still nearer it responds to the "correct" scent, to visual and chemical "honey guides" and to the entrance of the flower. Once it has settled, the scent of the nectar and guiding touch stimuli come into play. All these stimuli do more than elicit the next stage in the action chain and switch off the preceding act; they also activate the corresponding orientation mechanisms, with their target values.

Target values can also be changed by learning processes. The homing digger-wasp learns new landmarks with each new burrow it digs, and the crow returning to the place where it attacked the horned owl the year before does so because it learned this orientation. The salmon returning by scent to the river in which it grew up employs a learned target value. A special and still very puzzling case of a changing target value is the sun navigation of migrant birds. It has been established that starlings migrating south-west in autumn navigate by the sun. But in the three hours or so in the morning during which they do migrate, the sun turns over a considerable angle; yet the starlings keep their course. It has been shown that they change their target value with time; they have an "internal clock". How this internal clock works is still unknown.

A DIFFERENT orientation problem exists wherever a movement of part of the body, such as a limb, is steered by sense organs not situated on that limb, for instance by the eyes. How to explain a limb movement so fast that the eye cannot check its performance? The quick stroke of the forelimbs by which a praying mantis seizes a fly is such a movement. When a mantis sees a fly before it, it turns its head towards it. The rest of the body, on which the legs are situated, does not turn. Yet when the mantis strikes, its well-armed forelimbs hit the target with rarely failing precision. How do the forelimbs "know" what the eyes have seen—namely the precise direction of the fly with respect to the mantis's body? Remember that the strike is so fast that correction half way is not possible; even if the mantis can see where its forelimbs are going, it is already too late. Clearly the limb-aiming mechanism must be informed about the direction and extent of the preceding head movement. This is done by a second sense organ: pads of sensory hairs on the neck are pressed by the head when it turns. Thus the deformation of the hairs varies with the position of the head, and it is this which informs the central nervous system about the head position and hence the required direction of the strike. If one cuts the sensory nerves of the hair pads, the mantis strikes straight ahead, irrespective of the position of the head.

One could of course ask why the mantis turns its head at all. Why could not the visual information about the direction of the fly be transmitted directly to the centres controlling the direction of the stroke? The main reason for this may well be that the mantis must not merely know the direction in which the fly is seen but also its distance. This perception of distance is made possible by the use of two eyes, permitting binocular vision. A mantis with one eye would probably strike in the right direction at any object as long as it was seen under the correct angle—but it would probably overshoot small prey and undershoot large prey, since it would supposedly be judging distance by size.

So we see how manifold are the orientation mechanisms which each animal has to have available, and how, like so many other life processes, they serve to maintain a steady state. This particular steady state is the position and course to be maintained with respect to the spatial characteristics of the environment. And as in other life processes this is done by intricate systems of negative feedback: each deviation is reported and sets in motion exactly those movements which restore the orientated position. While an animal behaves, the required steady states change. The central nervous system is informed about these required changes and is "set" to the appropriate target values.

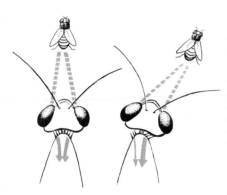

HOW TO CATCH A FLY

Many animal actions are made possible by information received by one part of the body and passed on to another. The praying mantis, for example, is informed of where to grab for a fly by the position of its head. If it spots a fly off to one side, it will turn its head towards the insect, as its eyes are immovable. This disturbs tiny hairs at each side of the head that send continuous nerve messages tending to keep the head directed straight forward. The nervous system measures the difference between two conflicting signals—one from the eyes to turn the head towards the prey, the other from the hairs to keep the head facing to the front—and this difference tells the forelegs where to aim. The drawings above show, first, a fly directly in front of the mantis, and signals of equal intensity (small arrows) being transmitted by the hairs at the sides of the head. The next drawing shows the head turned slightly and a stronger pressure (thicker arrow) acting on the hairs on that side.

STARTING A DOWNWARD DIVE, A GREYLAG GOOSE ROLLS OVER IN FLIGHT, BUT IT KEEPS ITS HEAD UPRIGHT TO AVOID BECOMING DISORIENTATED

A Sense of Direction

Every animal, at some time during its life, leaves one place and travels to another. Whether the journey covers a few inches for eating or mating, or whether it spans the globe during migration, the animal must have some type of sensory apparatus that will keep it headed in the appropriate direction. Many animals use familiar senses, but in others the mechanism is a complete mystery.

115

A Sonar-equipped Predator

A good sense of orientation is as important for predation as it is for navigation. The sonar that a bat uses when it negotiates a complicated maze also gives it a deadly advantage in the hunt. Following the echoes reflected from a moth, the bat may easily intercept it in one swift pass. This formidable tracking device has in turn forced moths to develop a number of adroit defensive countermeasures. A most remarkable adaptation is the ultrasonic "ears" on some moths' midsections; these organs can detect a bat's cries up to a hundred feet away, giving the insect enough warning to take evasive action. Other insects possess less sophisticated but none the less quite effective defences: their stingers or scratchy legs make for a singularly uncomfortable dinner—a mistake that most bats are unlikely to repeat.

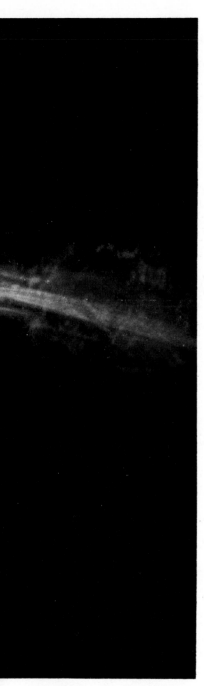

SCORING A BULL'S-EYE, a bat (*horizontal streak*) catches a frantically spiralling moth. The special photographic techniques on these pages were devised by bat expert F. A. Webster and his colleagues.

RECONSIDERING, the bat in this multiple-flash photograph rejects an intercepted moth. Sharp spurs probably make this species obnoxious; the bat may have recalled this from a prior bad experience.

A Three-dimensional Labyrinth for One-dimensional Rats

How would an animal's orientation be affected if it were reared in an environment so restricted that it could move only in one dimension? Would it be able to adjust to a three-dimensional world? Specifically, could a young rat so confined grow up to a normal, efficient adulthood? To answer these questions, University of Michigan behaviourist Eugene Harcum raised from birth three sets of rats in special mazes. The first was completely horizontal, the second was almost entirely made of vertical passage-ways, and the third allowed complete freedom to explore in all directions. After nine months under these conditions, each rat was transferred to a gargantuan three-dimensional maze (*opposite*), where its performance was recorded. The group that had grown up in three dimensions negotiated the maze with complete ease; the vertically orientated rats did nearly as well. But the horizontally orientated rats, never having been confronted with the concepts of "upness" or "downness", experienced a great deal of confusion before they could make their way through this strange new world.

INSERTING A RAT into a maze of 85 passage-ways, Harcum has draped his laboratory and himself with monotonous shrouds of colourless cloth to eliminate visual clues that might aid the rat in orientating.

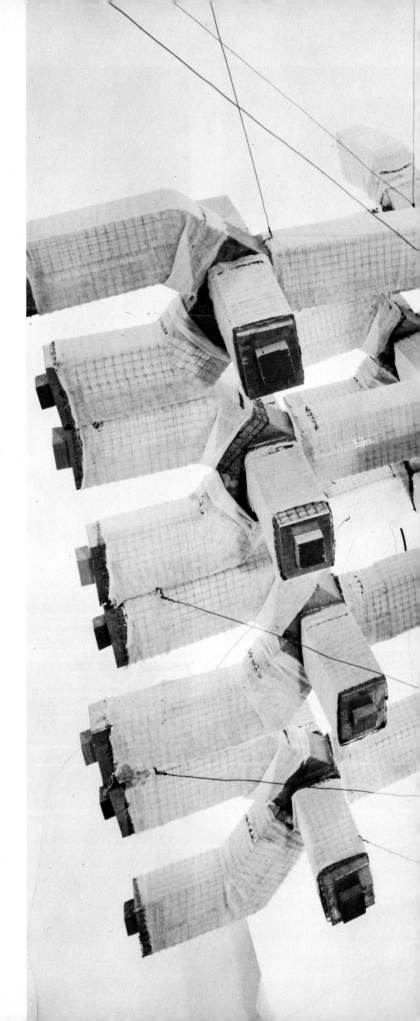

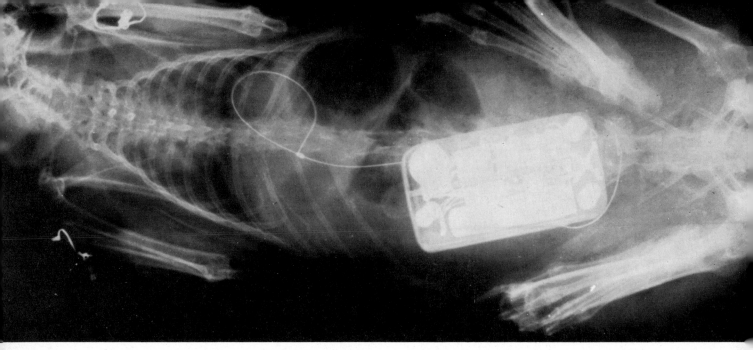

A HARE ON THE AIR, the rabbit in this X-ray photograph is sending out a steady stream of radio signals from a transmitter attached to electrodes monitoring its heart-beat. By correlating these data with the rabbit's observed behaviour, scientists may be able to learn exactly what physiological changes occur while the animal is adjusting to its environment.

AN ELECTRONIC SALMON, carrying a sealed transmitter, is followed by scientists with cathode-ray receivers. Before this, the best way was to tag one and await reports from fishermen.

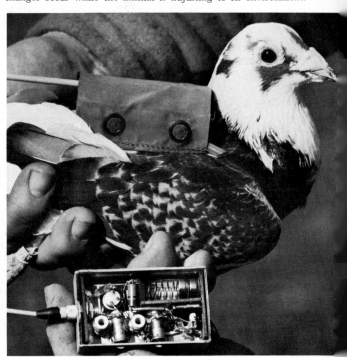

A PIGEON-BORNE RADIO can send signals for 20 hours up to 20 miles. This early model weighs more than two ounces and has a long antenna. Later models have been greatly improved.

Spying on Behaviour

At first glance, it might seem that scientists know quite a bit about how an animal migrates; in most cases they have learned where it starts, where it ends up and its approximate route. As useful as this information is, it still does not explain how animals orientate themselves during their journeys. Because of the pressing need for more precise information, behaviourists have teamed up with engineers in the new science of bio-telemetry. With tiny transistorized transmitters that can monitor a

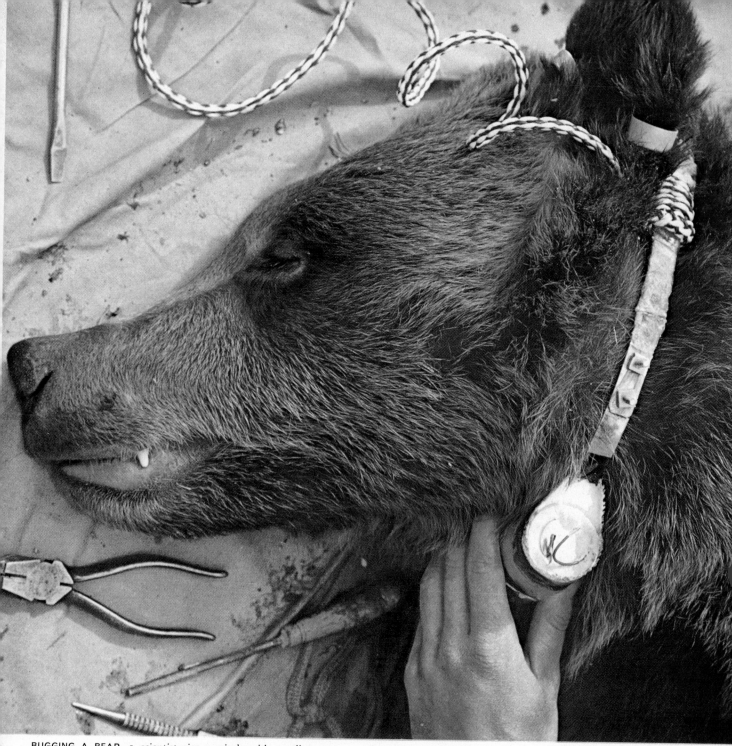

BUGGING A BEAR, a scientist rigs a grizzly with a collar antenna and batteries. By tracking it with portable equipment, researchers can compile precise data about the bear's selection of territory, daily and seasonal movements, hibernation and hunting habits. This bear was given a stiff sedative before scientists ventured to install its new electronic paraphernalia.

creature's respiration and heart-beat or pin-point subtle changes in its course, scientists are swiftly gathering enough data to make informed guesses about orientation. The areas that bio-telemetry opens to study are virtually boundless; the only restrictions are the weight and efficiency of the equipment. And engineers are constantly turning out smaller, more powerful, longer-lasting devices that will allow the animal to live its life completely unhindered—while scientists eavesdrop on its every action.

TOPSY-TURVY SQUIRREL-FISH in a cave in the Indian Ocean appear to have lost all sense of direction. Actually, the upside-down ones are orientating not to gravity but to light reflected from the white sandy bottom. The upright fish are in deep shadows, orientating only to gravity. This picture was taken by a camera-man whose flash-bulb obscured the actual light source.

Enigmas of Orientation

Some feats of orientation still defy any logical explanation. Squirrel-fish, for example, orientate with two different senses, sometimes with strange results (*above*). The lowly limpet has a homing ability that cannot be explained. Limpets scratch shallow depressions in rough rocky surfaces, which fit their shells closely, allowing them to conserve water at low tide and also to hold fast against any prying predators. Somehow they manage to find their way back to these "homes".

Waterfowl, like the lesser snow geese pictured here, orientate themselves visually—by the sun and by landmarks. But they often navigate without these aids; they fly above clouds, below clouds, between layers of clouds, in the daytime and at night, and they still arrive at their destinations. As a result, wondrous powers have been attributed to them, including an innate directional sense, magnetic field sensors, and even phenomenal luck.

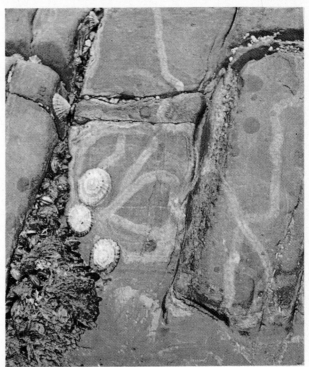

LIMPET TRACKS are marked on rock by these small marine creatures as they feed on algae. This foraging may carry them five feet from their home bases, but somehow they get back.

123

A HUMPBACK WHALE, in a remarkable photograph, leaps clear of the water during its migration to the Arctic Ocean. Each summer the humpbacks embark on a long journey to the brink of the polar ice-cap. There they remain until winter, gorging themselves on the plankton shrimp that abound in those waters. Each whale accumulates a great reserve of fat,

enough to sustain it through the return trip to its equatorial breeding grounds. On these trips whales apparently orientate themselves by sonar; they have excellent hearing and a wide variety of clicks and "rusty hinge" noises—strong evidence in favour of such a system. But how they could use it to navigate the immense expanse of miles-deep ocean is utterly unknown.

6

Instinct

v.

Learning

THERE is a catch phrase, still widely used though thoroughly outdated, which says that "animals act instinctively, but man acts intelligently". Like many such general statements, this could be interpreted in various ways, but it is generally taken to refer to the way behaviour develops in an individual— the point being that animals are born with a great deal of their adaptive be- haviour, so to speak, ready-made, whereas man must learn most of his. Of course, we know now that this is not altogether true, that there is a great deal more to the story of how behaviour, in all its intricate adaptability, develops in the course of an animal's life. This is the general story we shall consider now.

Many animals do not behave efficiently "from the word go", as a machine does, nor do animals keep the same behaviour patterns throughout their lives. Their behaviour machinery changes as they grow up—sometimes gradually, as a tadpole's wriggling in the egg case develops later into wavy swimming mo- tions for the water, or a human infant's walking evolves over a period of years. Some changes, on the other hand, are abrupt and spectacular: a newly hatched butterfly suddenly takes off and flies; an eider duckling two hours old makes a perfect splash dive into the water on its first try; a baby chimpanzee in the zoo suddenly turns a somersault and from then on does it often. Some changes occur early in life—a cuttle-fish just out of the egg very efficiently catches the first *Mysis* shrimp it sees—but others, like the reproductive activities of higher animals, occur much later. The changes we see most easily are those in the movements themselves, or motor patterns, as when your pet puppy learns to come when you whistle. However, such changes involve hidden parts of the machinery as well. You might think that what the puppy has learned is "running towards you"; actually he has learned "running towards you in response to a stimulus which did not elicit this behaviour before".

Our knowledge of such behaviour changes in the course of an animal's development is meagre, but we do know enough to say that the changes are often drastic and of many kinds. Consider, for example, the changing activities of a young gull in its first month of life.

THE chick's initial act in entering the world consists of pushing off the egg's "lid" through a series of forceful stretching movements of the neck. The special muscle used for this shrinks after it has done its duty. In the nest, the chick will at first lie quietly, brooded by the parent. In a few hours its downy plumage dries and becomes fluffy. Already before it is dry it will begin to make feeble pecking movements at the parent's bill tip whenever the parent bends down over the nest. These pecks increase rapidly in frequency, and perhaps in accuracy too, and soon the parent will respond by regurgitating food. The chick takes up this food and swallows it. During the next hours it will attempt to get up on its legs, at first in a half-hearted way, but soon it will stand upright.

Now fully in the world, the chick begins to preen its plumage. Before the day is out it will take a few clumsy steps, and when it is one day old it may even walk out of the nest. When the gull colony is disturbed by a predator the parents will fly up and call the alarm, whereupon the chick will crouch. When it is only a few days old the alarm call will elicit a considerably more complex response: the chick will first run out of the nest, enter cover and then crouch. Soon each chick on such occasions will run to one particular hiding place. Within a week a chick will begin to make flying movements. Within two weeks it will begin to call at strangers, and soon after it will dash at them and attack them.

Still later, the chick begins to feed independently. It starts by pecking indiscriminately at many different objects, but after a while it ignores inedible objects and eats only real food. The flying movements become stronger, and when the chick is four to five weeks old it can fly. But its landing is still very clumsy; at first it will alight without regard for wind direction and force, and it may tumble over two or three times when it lands with a strong tail wind. When it sees water for the first time, it may dip its bill into it and may then drink. But while at first it will try to drink from any glittering surface, it will soon recognize water as such. After drinking, it may begin to make bathing movements, but days will pass before it will actually bathe in the water. At first it may even make these movements while standing on land, but facing the water that has wetted its bill.

This is typical of how behaviour develops in many animals. Some movements are performed reasonably well or even perfectly the first time they are done; others develop gradually. At a glance one is inclined to say of the first type that they must be innate, and that the second type of development reveals a gradual learning. Consider, for instance, the way the chick crouches the first time the parent gulls fly up in alarm. This looks like non-learned behaviour, and it may well be; but on the other hand, the chick could have heard the alarm call before, while still in the egg, and it may have associated this with the chilling caused by the exposure of the eggs. Thus crouching could originally have been a response to chilling and only later associated with the alarm call.

Conversely, the gradual development of the flying movement would seem to be due to the chick's continuous practising. This has been tested in experiments with young pigeons reared in narrow earthenware tubes in which they simply could not make the necessary practising movements. Yet when the "tube birds" were released for the first time, simultaneously with normal young of the same age who had just learned to fly, they flew just as well as the normal birds! Obviously the gradual improvement observed under normal conditions can occur without practice; the clumsy nature of the chick's early attempts may well have been due simply to the fact that the urge to fly was there before the wings and the flying muscles were fully developed.

This goes to show that mere observations, however precise, can be misleading. If we want to get reliable information as to whether a certain type of behaviour changes through learning or develops innately (or perhaps through a combination of the two processes), we have to do experiments. But before I discuss some of the experiments that have been done it will be useful to formulate our problem a little more clearly.

The phenomenon we want to explain is that of change in behaviour mechanics during development. These changes are many. The appearance of a new behaviour pattern, or its disappearance or, perhaps most often, the perfection of a behaviour pattern—all these things are changes and can be readily seen. But an animal's sensitivity to stimuli changes too. Thus, the mere observation and description of these developments of behaviour, no matter how carefully recorded, are no more than a start. Considerably more difficult is finding out how these changes are brought about: what causes each change.

THE first step in such an analysis is in principle the same as in many other behaviour studies: we distinguish between causes within the animal and those acting on it from outside.

Let us consider outside causes first. When a young gosling hatches from the egg, it is soon able to walk. This walking is directed: it begins to follow its mother. After it has followed the mother for some time, it will not follow other animals. But if we hatch a gosling in an incubator and present it, not with its mother, but with another animal or even something like a blue balloon, it will follow this abnormal object. And once it has followed the balloon for some time, it will continue to do so and refuse to follow a real mother goose. In behaviour terms, it has become "imprinted" on the artificial parent—on whatever elicited its "following response" first.

What this shows is that in order to behave normally—i.e., to follow its mother —the gosling had to be exposed to the mother first. To use an engineering term, the "programming" of the "following response" was not complete at hatching. Whatever the gosling might have had in the way of an innate response had to be supplemented by exposure to the outside world.

In other cases no such supplementary programming is required: the response is clearly not learned. If we hatch a black-headed gull chick in an incubator, keep it in complete darkness for a few hours and then show it models of the parent's bill, we find that it responds more vigorously to red models—the natural colour of the adult's bill—than to those of any other colour. Since the chick

**CAN BABY CHICKS TELL
DUCKS FROM HAWKS?**

*Since the young chicks of many kinds of
fowl crouch in alarm when the silhou-
ette of a hawk passes overhead but ignore
the shapes of other harmless birds like
ducks, behaviourists concluded that there
was an inborn ability to tell the difference between the short-necked predators
(coloured silhouettes, above) and longer-
necked, harmless species. More recent research, however, has shown that there is
a different explanation (opposite page).*

had never seen anything, and certainly not an adult gull, its programming with
respect to bill colour must have been done internally.

From these two examples it is clear that the mechanics of behaviour can be programmed either from within or from without. The external programming is
done through individual adjustments through experience. The internal programming, as we shall see later, is the result of the slow evolution of the animal
itself. It was achieved through long interaction with the environment in a kind
of gambling—a trial-and-error process—which through generation after generation gave natural selection the chance to weed out failures and preserve the
efficiently programmed types.

LIKE the "following response", many other behaviour patterns develop through
individual interaction with the environment. One of the simplest is probably just getting used to a stimulus. An example of this is the response of many
young pheasants, chickens and turkeys to the sight of moving objects overhead.
Without having been in any way taught to do so, they crouch down or show
some other form of alarm behaviour—a behaviour pattern that clearly has to do
with defence against a predator. However, after a few such experiences, their
crouching response wanes: they lose this general fear of birds or objects flying
overhead. In other words, their sensitivity to the stimuli gradually decreases.
This process, called habituation, is very useful, because obviously if young birds
were to crouch down every time another bird flew past they would be losing a
great deal of time in needless alarm behaviour.

Does this mean that chicks, as they grow older, get used to *all* birds flying
overhead? Not at all, and that is the subtle and fascinating thing about habituation. Chicks become habituated only to shapes that they see repeatedly—such
as song-birds or even falling leaves. Those that are new or strange to them will
still alarm them. Since birds of prey are much less numerous than non-predatory
species, chicks have little chance to get used to them, and when a hawk flies
overhead a chick will crouch, although it will pay no attention to a flock of
sparrows. The fact that the chick has no way of knowing that a hawk is dangerous, having never experienced an attack from one, makes its crouch look like
an innate response. Actually it is not. It is the result of a "gap" in the chick's
habituation. Having learned what shapes are *not* harmful, it confines its crouching to shapes which could still be harmful until proved otherwise by familiarity.

Learning *not* to crouch is a negative process. There are others which are just
the opposite, in which the animal learns to *do* something—in short, to respond
to a stimulus to which it was originally indifferent. This process was made
famous by the researches of Ivan Petrovich Pavlov, who would, for instance, ring
a bell every time he gave a dog food. After many such experiences, the dog
would drool in anticipation whenever the bell was rung. The point, of course, is
that a dog does not normally drool at the ringing of a bell but can be taught to
do so. This learning process occurs widely in nature. Birds of prey show it by
returning regularly to places where they have successfully hunted. So does my
cat, which runs to the kitchen when it hears me sharpening the carving knife.

The action of a running cat or a drooling dog is positive, something that the
animal has learned to do. Slightly puzzling are positive actions that look like
negative ones. What would we say about a pike that learned *not* to hunt sticklebacks? Positive or negative? Naïve young pike will often try to snap up sticklebacks, only to find that the raised spines of the smaller fish prevent them
from being swallowed. After a few such experiences, pike stop hunting stickle-

backs. Although this looks like habituation, it is not. The pike has not become used to sticklebacks; it has learned the entirely positive fact that spiky little fish cannot be swallowed and might as well be avoided. The anti-predator defences of many small animals depend on this ability of predators to learn from experience. This is the reason why many insects display so-called warning colours, broadcasting the fact that they are either poisonous or distasteful or merely hard-shelled: birds learn to reject them on sight after they have tried them. All these examples differ from habituation: the animals do not become merely insensitive to the stimuli but positively change their response to them.

Learning by imitation, though rare among animals, is still another form of interacting with the environment. Something like it is found in some song-birds that learn to sing properly only by listening to others of their species. If young chaffinches are raised without hearing other chaffinches sing, they do not develop their normal song; all they produce is a kind of "unintelligible" warble. But if, in their formative weeks, they can hear the song of experienced males, they develop the normal song of the species. Some species of birds possess this gift of song imitation to a high degree, the world champion probably being the mynah bird of India.

A German colleague of mine did an amusing experiment on this subject with bullfinches. He had one young male raised by a female canary, and this bird, surrounded by other canaries, acquired their song, imitating it so exactly that its song could not be distinguished from that of a true canary. Later, this bullfinch mated with a female of its own species and the pair raised young together. Two males of this brood learned the canary song from their father and sang it perfectly when they were grown up. One of these was sent to an aviarist two miles away and mated there with a female bullfinch. When, two years later, one of the sons of this pair, a grandson of the original male, was returned to my colleague, it rewarded him by singing like a canary too—the song taught four years previously to its grandfather!

THE acquisition of motor skills by practice is also widespread. Although, as we have seen, birds need not learn the basic pattern of flight, they probably do not acquire perfect skill without practice. I mentioned earlier that young gulls have to learn to land against the wind. This is probably true of many birds, and it seems that in general the art of landing is difficult and has to be learned. Many young birds even find the first stages of descent difficult —once airborne, they fly higher and higher and may be carried off in a strong wind, get lost and perish.

All these examples of learning have two things in common: the behaviour is not perfect the first time it is shown, and to improve it the animal must acquire experience of some kind. The reason that the young chicks gradually stopped crouching was simply the experience that nothing dreadful happened.

The most complex interactions with the environment probably occur in monkeys and apes, and in our own species. Harry F. Harlow and his co-workers at the University of Wisconsin are carrying out fascinating studies of behaviour development in rhesus monkeys. While, as we shall see presently, the innate equipment of most lower animals is relatively complete and often efficient from the start that of Harlow's monkeys turned out to be much less elaborate; rather it consisted of a set of relatively vague, general urges and needs, which had to be developed by continuous interplay with the environment. Basic among these needs is that for security—which a normal rhesus mother provides above

YES, BUT THEY MUST LEARN THE DIFFERENCE

The clue to the timid crouching of chicks lies in their innate tendency to do this when anything passes overhead—harmless as well as harmful birds—and even to cringe at falling leaves (top drawing). As they grow older, they slowly get used to these common objects (middle drawing) and lose their fear of them. However, they never become accustomed to the unfamiliar shapes of predators (bottom drawing), because these birds are rare.

131

all by allowing the baby to cling to her body. Infants deprived of this and other expressions of motherly care are too frightened to venture out on any exploratory excursions and so fail to acquire the absolutely vital experience of the outside world. The same deprivation has no less disastrous effects on the infants' later social life: they fail to develop co-operative bonds with their companions, and even to mate normally, becoming either very aggressive or indifferent.

Similar things have been found in other mammals as well, such as cats, rats and goats. There can be little doubt that many of these findings apply likewise to human infants—in fact, we rely even more on experience.

Such is human nature that when we look too eagerly for one thing we may fail to see others. Too concentrated a search for all kinds of effects of experience may blind us to the fact that in the majority of animals much of the programming of the behaviour machinery is done internally. Even when behaviour is moulded by interplay with the environment, this moulding means no more than a change of a behaviour that was already functioning, and may even have been functioning fairly well. For example, while young goslings do learn to follow the object to which they are first exposed, their very first response is not just random: they walk—which is itself a co-ordinated movement of considerable complexity, even though it is not perfect the first time—and they do not follow just anything, they prefer objects that move, that are of a certain size range, and that have certain other characteristics. We have also seen that the first flight of a pigeon and the first flight of a butterfly, while perhaps not perfect, are at least extremely competent. We also know that the displays of many species of fishes and birds are not learned; they develop normally in animals that have been raised alone, and even in those that have had foster parents of other species.

Oᴜʀ knowledge of these matters is still extremely patchy. Yet we are beginning to see that on the one hand most animals are fairly well programmed internally but that on the other hand they often require a variety of "adjusting instructions" from their environment in order to reach the remarkable efficiency they show when adult. It is good to express oneself cautiously here because a satisfactory terminology has not yet been generally agreed on. Particular care has to be exercised in the use of the term "innate", for this term has led to misunderstandings because different people attach different meanings to it. The issue is a difficult semantic one, but I shall try to clarify it with an example.

Suppose that we are discussing the fighting behaviour of male three-spined sticklebacks in breeding condition. These fish, as we know, attack red objects more than other objects. We make an experiment to see if this behaviour is innate or learned by experience: we isolate some sticklebacks while they are still in the egg, and we never let them see another fish or any object of a similar size until they are fully mature and ready to breed. Then, and only then, do we show them another male stickleback in breeding condition or a dummy with a red belly which simulates a breeding male; our isolated fishes will attack it.

This may sound straightforward enough. Since our fishes, in their isolation, could not possibly have learned to attack competitors, it would seem their behaviour must be innate. But to demonstrate that certain learning processes are *not* required for a normal development is not really the same as to say that the behaviour is innate. To prove innateness, we must show that no interplay with the environment has been necessary at all. And our procedure did not fully eliminate all possible effects that the environment might have had. For instance, it could well be that at an earlier stage the growing eyes of these sticklebacks needed to be exposed to light in order to start functioning properly. At any rate, this has been found to be the case in the development of tadpoles and some higher animals. The same might be true of sticklebacks too—we simply have not explored this. Therefore, if by "innate" we mean "programmed completely without control by the environment", then we cannot describe the sticklebacks' attack behaviour as innate as we have not investigated possible environmental effects on such earlier phases of the development.

However, if we mean by "innate" that a fully developed fish, once all its senses are functioning, shows co-ordinated and complex behaviour without practice, conditioning or imitation, then we can properly call this innate, since *as an integrated whole* it requires no experience. Yet even so, the term can be misunderstood—which leads us to another important aspect of the problem. Let us observe a newly hatched chick as it first starts to feed. It will peck at the first grain it sees, but its aim will be very poor. In only a few days, however, its aim will improve markedly. Is not this learning—the result of experience, in which a good peck is rewarded with a grain of corn and a poor one with nothing? It would certainly seem so, but this conclusion has been proved false in an ingenious experiment in which eyeglasses with special lenses were fitted to chicks. These lenses made the grains of corn appear to be half an inch to one side of where they really were. Obediently the chicks aimed where they thought the grain was. Their pecks were poor at first, but as before, they improved in accuracy as the chicks grew older, although this accuracy was always misdirected by the glasses. The chicks never got any grain at all, and the increased concentration of their pecks—at the wrong target—was obviously the result of something other than learning by being rewarded with food. What it actually was we do not yet know. It may have been something as unexpected as the fact that the chicks were becoming increasingly steady on their legs and thus could peck more accurately.

Whichever use of the word "innate" we prefer, we still can prove nothing about the internal programming of an animal by subjecting it to external tests. We can isolate it, rear it in darkness, in silence, and all we can show is that *these* things do not influence development. This is negative evidence, an attempt to prove something by elimination. It does not demonstrate that the behavioural machinery does grow internally—let alone how. For real proof, we must unravel the growth processes themselves. Therefore, just as outside control can be proved only by raising animals under varied external conditions, so internal control has to be studied through interfering with internal conditions.

Experiments of the latter kind have as yet not been done on any large scale, but one example is worth mentioning in some detail. If we tickle the skin on the back of a frog, it will respond by scratching the tickled spot with a well-aimed movement of its leg. Tickle its belly, and the frog will scratch its belly. This is possible because sensory nerves running from each part of the skin to the spinal cord provide the frog with information about the spot where it was stimulated. Now, if at a very early stage of development—namely, before the nerves growing out from the spinal cord have actually made contact with the skin—we exchange a bit of back skin on a frog with a bit of belly skin, we will in due course see something surprising. After the nerves have had time to make connection between the skin and the spinal cord, this particular frog, if tickled on the back, will scratch its belly—and vice versa!

This fascinating experiment allows only one explanation, and a very startling

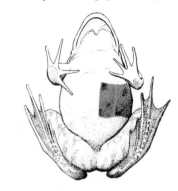

133

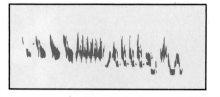

"EDUCATED" SONG

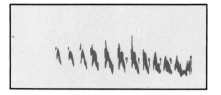

"UNEDUCATED" SONG

MUST CHAFFINCHES
BE TAUGHT TO SING?

Many birds learn their songs by listening to adults of their own species; this can be tested by rearing young birds away from their own kind and then recording what they produce on their own. The top spectrogram is a visual recording of the song of a wild chaffinch. It has a varied pattern that falls into four distinct parts and sounds something like: chip-chip-chip-chip, tell-tell-tell-tell, cherry-erry-erry-erry, tissy-che-wee-ooo. The lower spectrogram shows the song of a laboratory chaffinch that had never heard another chaffinch sing. It is a monotonous cherry-erry-erry, tissy-issy-issy and, while it retains a vaguely chaffinch-like quality, it is not nearly so elaborate as the normal chaffinch song, showing that while some singing ability is innate, much of it must be learned.

one at that. To start with, it should be stressed that the two patches of skin developed normally even though transplanted. The piece of back skin grew dark green although it was on the white belly, and the piece of belly skin grew white even though on the back—which proved that there were chemical differences in them from the beginning. These chemical differences apparently made themselves known to the nerves, in effect saying, "I am a piece of back skin" or "I am a piece of belly skin", no matter where they were located. In short, the function of the nerve, undetermined at first, was settled once and for all by the chemical nature of the bit of skin into which it had grown, and not by the location of that bit of skin.

Here, then, is a direct experimental indication of a particular kind of internal programming, for the skin programmes its sensory nerves. How this takes place is still unknown, but the evidence that it does happen is clear—and the proof does not rest on elimination of outside effects, but on real interference with internal development processes.

So far, we know almost nothing about the nature of internal control of the development of behaviour, and still far too little about the equally complicated problem of how it is affected by external experience. Students of learning all over the world are testing theories of the ways in which experience changes behaviour and also are trying hard to disentangle the internally controlled events. Yet, so intricate are the processes that this field of research, one of the most challenging and most crucial for our understanding of behaviour, is still in its infancy.

We have learned a few things. We know, for instance, that many complex behaviour patterns are neither all internal nor all external but a combination of the two, as shown by the way squirrels crack hazel-nuts. A hazel-nut has a groove in its shell, and an experienced squirrel will grasp the nut in such a way that it can gnaw at this groove, quickly deepening it. Then it will turn the nut around in its "hands", give it a quick, hard bite and the nut will crack open. This extremely efficient procedure contrasts strongly with that of a young squirrel which has been raised on other kinds of food and which has had no opportunity to practice manipulating, gnawing and cracking. True, it will start as if it were the most skilful gnawer in squirreldom. It will grasp the nut, turning it over and over and gnawing away with great energy, just as an experienced squirrel will, and after an appropriate interval, it will try to crack the nut open. However, all these efforts are very ineffective; instead of holding the nut so that it can gnaw at the groove, it gnaws all over the surface, and as a result its cracking efforts are in vain, and it has to start over again. In short, the squirrel is programmed internally for manipulating, for gnawing and for cracking, but it must learn by experience how to do these things well.

Another example of the joint action of innate ability and improvement by learning is provided by the song learning of chaffinches. We have seen that isolated chaffinches develop a kind of warbling song which is very different from the normal song of the species. Yet this song does show some unmistakable characteristics—for instance a rather chaffinch-like rhythm. Further, while it is also true that such isolated birds can learn a variety of songs, the song they learn most readily is that of their own species. This means that although they learn, the things they will learn best are themselves determined by internal programming.

What is more, these specific abilities and inclinations to learn change in the course of an animal's life. Many things are learned only at certain times. A duckling or a gosling is not at all times equally "imprintable". If ducklings are hatched alone in an incubator and, instead of being shown a mother or a substitute soon after hatching, are kept locked up for a few days, they have all but lost the ability to become imprinted. The tendency to follow a mother and learn what she looks like appears soon after hatching, reaches a peak in a few hours and then gradually wanes. This applies to other things as well— it is probable that many birds have to acquire the finer skills of flying in the first few months after fledging, and that this becomes more difficult if they are prevented from practising. Digger-wasps even learn their landmarks in the few seconds it takes them to make their locality studies. In other words, there are "critical periods" in the lives of animals when they are more ready to learn certain things than they are at other times. It is of course part of our task to find out what determines the onset and the end of such critical periods.

The study of animals in their natural surroundings has revealed many examples of these deep-rooted determinants of the readiness to learn. Bumble-bees out foraging for nectar-yielding plants will, when they come upon a new one, make a quick locality study of it so that they can find it again. But they do not do this with all plants. Some, like foxgloves, have such large and conspicuous flowers that they can be seen and located from a distance. It is only the more unobtrusive ones with small blossoms that prompt a bee to make a locality study. The usefulness of this is clear; but what determines whether or not the bee will "decide" to learn is anything but clear.

It will surprise nobody that an ape is more intelligent than a rabbit. Similarly, crows, parrots and geese are more intelligent than hawks, gulls or chickens. These differences in over-all learning ability and general intelligence occur throughout the animal kingdom. What is less well known is that there are equally profound differences that do not necessarily depend on over-all intelligence. Guillemots are no more intelligent than gulls, and yet they always learn to recognize their own eggs, which gulls do not. Gulls are potentially clever enough to do this, and their eggs are different enough to permit it. Why, then, do they not do so? The answer is that they have another way of locating their nests—by learning the lie of the landmarks round about them. Provided it is in the right place, a gull will accept anything that looks anything like an egg, even a potato, as its own.

WHAT strikes the naturalist about these differences between species is that each species develops its behaviour in a way that seems best suited to its needs. The guillemots have to learn to recognize their own eggs because they do not build nests, and their eggs may roll about on the rock ledges. It is useful to a bumble-bee to learn the location of a plant with small flowers that cannot be seen from a distance. What we learn from all this is that it is not only the complete, fully developed behaviour that is efficient but also the way it develops.

This conclusion, which is as yet no more than tentative as far as details are concerned, is very obvious when we consider the gross differences between species or between behaviour patterns within a species. It is clearly of great advantage to a bird to be able to fly well the first time it tries, particularly if it nests on a cliff or high up in a tree. The presence of numerous efficient predators makes this a must—it is simply too dangerous to have to learn flying clumsily and slowly the way we learn to walk or swim. On the other hand, it would be a handicap to a bird if its innate knowledge of what constituted acceptable food were too specialized. By trying out a large variety of things and learning by experience to concentrate on food that is good for it and that is at the same time abundant, a particular species will manage to make the most of different habitats and different seasons of the year. Behaviour development therefore poses the same problem as the finished behaviour: we must not only unravel the mechanisms controlling development but we must also investigate in detail how the developmental control in each species meets the peculiar needs of that species.

And what about our own species? How does man fit into this picture? Of course we know that we learn a great deal, but do we also have a basic, internally programmed repertoire? This is extremely difficult to decide, for we do not want to carry out experiments on our fellow humans, and certainly not the kind of drastic experiments that would be required. We would not allow anybody to raise a baby in isolation. We have therefore to rely on incidental (clinical) and indirect evidence.

THE indications are that the bulk of human internal programming supplies us with relatively simple units of behaviour in response to simple stimuli— with motor patterns like eye blinking, yawning, weeping and smiling, the basic pattern of locomotion and such simple responses as the flicking movements by which we brush an insect off our skin. In addition, we probably have some kind of internal programming at higher levels, such as the specific responsiveness in men to certain complex stimuli supplied by women, and vice versa. We should also mention aggressive behaviour and motherly nursing behaviour patterns. But in the absence of really decisive evidence, we have to be very cautious about our conclusions. An extra reason for caution is that a mammalian embryo may undergo external influences and gather experience while still in the womb. It has been shown, for instance, that human babies show differences in certain leg reflexes according to the position (head down or head up) in which they have spent their pre-natal life.

The general problem, that of "nature or nurture", is of supreme importance since issues of the greatest urgency depend on its solution. To what extent can we manipulate man's aggressiveness through educational measures, for example? To what extent can we control man's willingness to be taught? What about the very techniques of teaching? With questions like these unanswered, it is not surprising that the development of behaviour is being studied intensely in our nearest relatives, the other primates. We have already seen that much of the adult social behaviour of higher mammals, particularly monkeys and apes, is profoundly influenced by the relations an animal has had with its mother when young. Experiencing normal motherly love (that is, the entire, intricate treatment a loving mother bestows on her infant) is necessary for the development of later social behaviour of many kinds. Clinical evidence with human beings shows that this is true of our species as well.

But clinical evidence can never be as convincing as experiments, and much of our understanding of the development of human behaviour will have to come from the study of behaviour in animals. Nor should we confine such studies to our nearest relatives—just as in the medical sciences, which have long since relied on experiments on a wide variety of creatures, we need to get our facts from as many different sources as we can. And this application of our work to the understanding of man may in the end be the most important justification of animal behaviour studies—even though it is a selfish one.

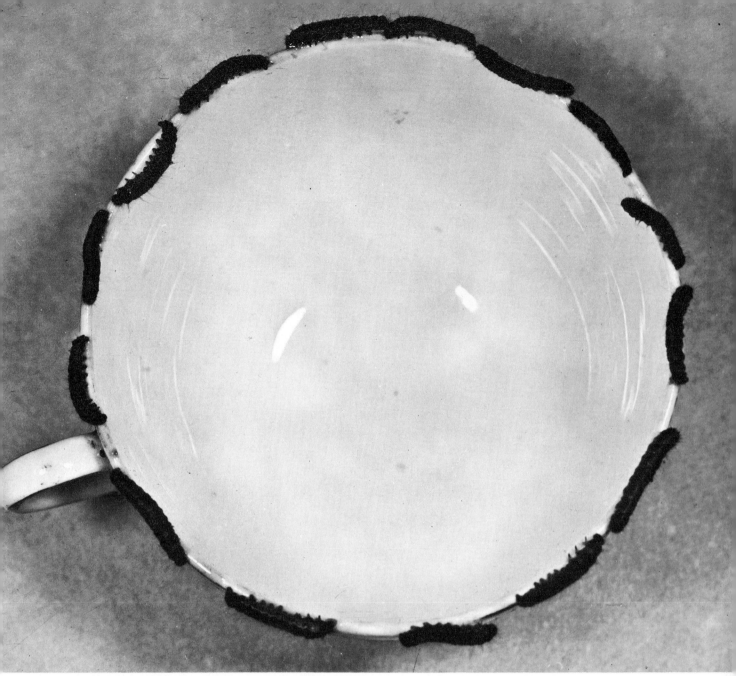

TRAPPED BY THEIR RIGID INSTINCT TO FOLLOW EACH OTHER ON BRANCHES, CATERPILLARS TRUDGE ENDLESSLY ROUND THE RIM OF A CUP

What Can Animals Learn?

Certain behaviour patterns are as thoroughly inbred as any physical attribute, others are wholly acquired, but most are subtle combinations of the two. To understand why animals act the way they do, it is essential to separate the innate from the learned. Untold hours of painstaking scrutiny, in laboratory and field, are being spent to unravel that puzzle, often with surprising results.

A TIN MAZE, a turtle, and a dish of water provide a simple answer to the question: can turtles, known for their limited intelligence, learn? The answer is yes, they can. Just as turtles in nature find their way round their stream-side homes, this one eventually learned to ignore the dead ends and waddle straight down the path to the water. However, it took 38 tries.

Some Lessons from the Laboratory

Many questions concerning the relationship between instinct and learning are best answered in the laboratory. The chick on the right, for instance, is part of an experiment devised by a University of Chicago psychologist, Eckhard H. Hess. His problem was to determine whether baby chicks, which demonstrably improve their pecking accuracy as they grow, do so as a result of maturing in their neuromuscular equipment or whether they actually learn by trial and error. Contrary to Hess's expectation, the former hypothesis proved true—the chicks improved simply because they were growing older. Hess calls this "the natural unfolding of innate processes"—as opposed to behaviour which becomes more efficient as a result of experience or learning. Interestingly, even human babies develop in part this way. In one experiment, identical twins were separated, one kept on flat surfaces while learning to crawl, the other given extensive experience with stairs. Later, when the child accustomed only to flat surfaces was introduced to stairs for the first time, it was found to climb just as well as its twin.

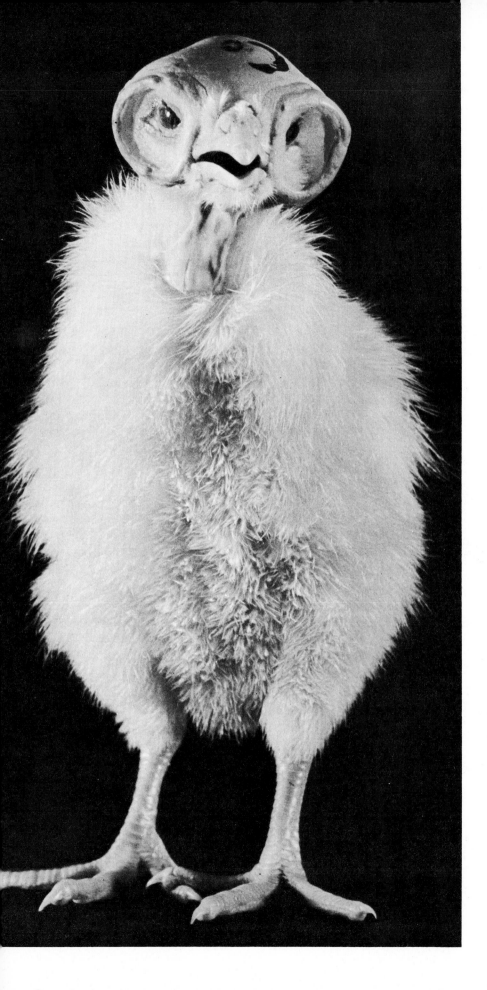

A GOGGLED CHICK provides data on the learning process. Prisms in the goggles deflect its vision to the right; whereas most higher animals would soon learn to adjust for this, the chick cannot, as shown below.

PECK MARKS aimed at a simulated seed set in soft clay prove the point. The top two patterns were made three days apart by a chick without prisms, the bottom two by a chick with prisms. In each case aim improves with maturity, but after three days the chick with prisms still pecks to the right of the mark.

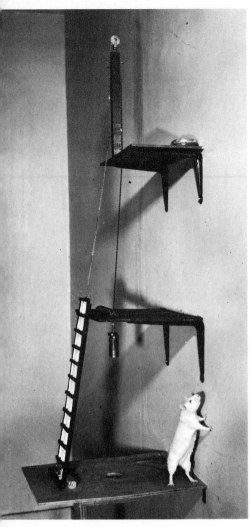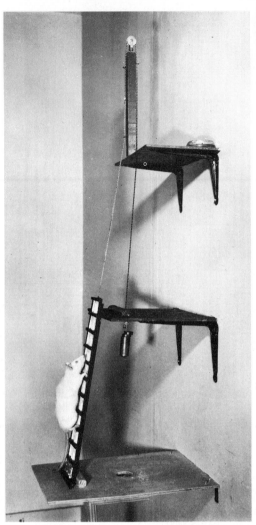

A WHITE RAT FACES THE TRICKY PROBLEM OF GETTING CHEESE, WHICH IS PLACED ON A HIGH SHELF WITH NO LADDER LEADING UP TO IT. HE U

Tests for Thinking Rats

Psychologists once believed that man and apes held a monopoly on reason. When behaviour which appeared to be based on reason was observed in lower species, it was attributed to a combination of instinct and accidental trial-and-error learning. Suspecting that no such precise division among animals existed, Loh Seng Tsai, a Tulane University psychologist, began in 1929 experimenting with laboratory rats. His results eloquently bear out his supposition.

Tsai's white rats, through a process of breeding and training, are a far cry from their natural cousins. Admittedly no sewer rat has performed these feats. Nevertheless, a rat is a rat for all that, and if the innate ability to find solutions to complicated problems were not characteristic of the species, results like these could never have been obtained.

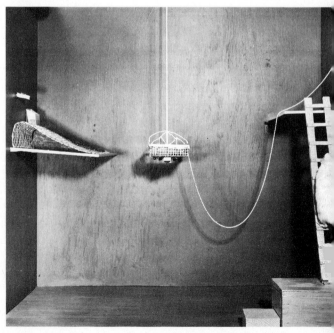

IN ANOTHER TEST, A RAT CLIMBS TO A SHELF OPPOSITE ONE WITH CHEE

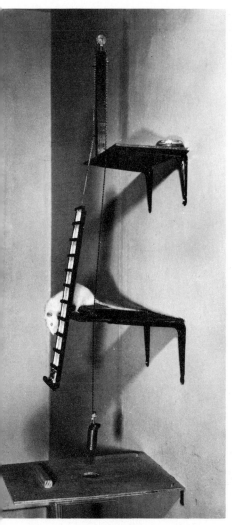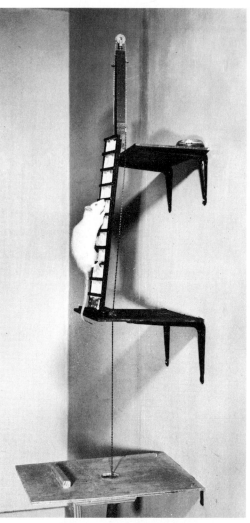

…E LADDER TO REACH THE LOWER SHELF AND HAULS IT UP AFTER HIM, CHECKING ONCE TO SEE HOW IT IS COMING. THEN HE CLIMBS TO THE TOP

…E FINDS THE CHAIN TIED TO THE BASKET, PULLS THE BASKET TO HIM, THEN SWINGS ACROSS TO THE CHEESE SHELF AND COLLECTS HIS REWARD

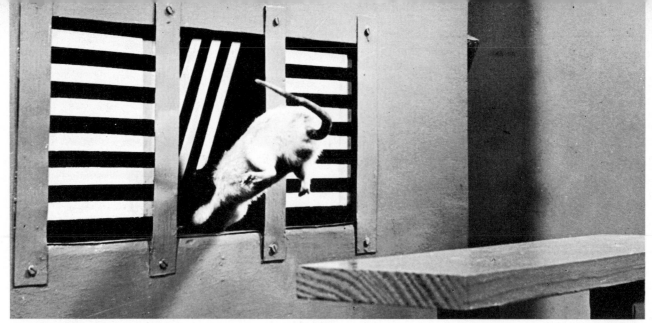

AFTER CHEESE, A RAT LEAPS FROM A SHELF THROUGH ONE OF THREE DOORS. THE TWO WITH SIMILAR STRIPES ARE LATCHED, THE OTHER OPEN

THE RAT JUMPS AGAIN (ABOVE AND BELOW), EACH TIME CHOOSING THE PROPER DOOR, PROVING IT HAS GRASPED THE CONCEPT OF "ODDNESS"

STARS OF THE MOSCOW CIRCUS, A PAIR OF EUROPEAN BROWN BEARS CROWN THEIR ACT WITH THIS PICK-A-BACK TURN ON A MOTOR CYCLE

Training the Trainable

Add to an animal's native intelligence the patient and persuasive hand of the trainer, and the results, as these pictures show, can be astounding. It is axiomatic that training capitalize on an animal's natural abilities. The bears above, no matter how clever and willing, could never have been taught to ride the motor cycle had they not initially been able to hold its handle-bar. This is equally true where mental processes are concerned. Both rats and bears

are canny animals, used to working out the easy way of doing things. Thus they are receptive to rewards and, for that matter, punishments, such as the bump on the nose the rat at the left gets when it jumps at the wrong door. On the other hand, rewards mean nothing to the big circus cats. These carnivores must be psychologically dominated by their trainer, just as in nature they are dominated by another cat—hence the trainer's whip and pistol.

143

FIRST ATTEMPT to open a hazel-nut is made by an adult squirrel which has never seen a nut before. Gnawing tenaciously, the squirrel at last succeeds but leaves a ragged shell (*left*) scarred by many false starts.

When Practice Makes Perfect

In an ingenious experiment to test learning processes through practice, Irenäus Eibl-Eibesfeldt of the Max Planck Institute in Germany raised squirrels in natural surroundings but without any seeds or nuts to practice on until they were adult. He wanted to find out whether the simple and elegant way in which experienced squirrels open hazel-nuts was "perhaps an inborn trait and whether what appeared to be learning was actually maturation in disguise". He quickly found that although squirrels recognize, manipulate and crack nuts instinctively, it is only by trial and error that they learn to do it efficiently.

This learned skill at opening nuts may be contrasted with the squirrel's urge to hide them, which is entirely innate. This makes good sense, as Eibl-Eibesfeldt points out, since squirrels eat so many different kinds of nuts and fruit pips that no single method of opening them would work for all. However, should squirrels have to learn to hide nuts by experience, they might not survive their first winter.

A SECOND TRY shows improvement. After opening several more nuts, the squirrel has learned to concentrate on one particular part of the shell. The result is neater than the first but is still very time-consuming.

FURTHER IMPROVEMENT shows after more practice. The squirrel starts at the soft end of the nut, gnaws connecting furrows and breaks out a piece. Still it has not found the best way, but it is close.

TRIUMPH! The meat comes out in one piece. The squirrel has finally found the natural grooves that exist in hazel-nuts, chiselled them deeper and cracked the nut with almost no waste effort. This experiment proves that, whereas the urge to open a nut, to hold it and gnaw it is instinctive, combining these behaviour patterns into a well-co-ordinated attack on one particular kind of nut is an acquired skill.

Once Bitten, Twice Shy

Mimicry is most often considered from the point of view of the mimic—how good is its disguise? One tends to forget that mimicry, no matter how ingenious, will not work at all if the predator lacks the intelligence to be fooled or does not care what it eats. In some lower species of predators the choice of foods is automatic from birth, but often a predator's tastes are acquired. These 10 pictures, part of an experiment conducted at the Archbold Biological Station in Florida by Lincoln and Jane Brower in the course of their investigation into mimicry, illustrate how this learning process takes place in the case of a southern toad. This toad's normal diet is insects, and its instinct is to snap up anything that wiggles like one. Up to the point of these pictures, this particular toad had seen neither a bumble-bee nor its stingless and quite palatable mimic, the robber-fly. Out of this experience came a useful lesson about bees, and though in the future it may be fooled by robber-flies and miss a potential meal or two, its ability to learn serves it well, since the sting of a bumble-bee can be extremely serious for a toad.

3 Next the toad is offered a robber-fly, a close mimic of the bumble-bee but lacking the bumble-bee's capacity to sting.

4 The toad, which has as yet never eaten a bumble-bee, gobbles up the robber-fly as quickly as it did the dragon-fly.

7 When a second bumble-bee is offered, the toad will not snap at it and ducks its head, having learned its lesson.

8 Now a robber-fly is offered. Again the toad refuses, taking the fly for a bee, showing the fly's mimicry to be effective.

1 To begin the experiment, a palatable dragon-fly is danced on the end of a thread in front of a hungry southern toad.

2 With a gulp the toad seizes the bait, the wings and abdomen of which protrude. Toads only snap at moving insects.

5 Now a bumble-bee is dangled. Like the other baits, it was purposely exhausted and cannot fly—but it can still sting.

6 And it does! The toad rises to the bait, but this time it gets a violent sting on its tongue and spits out the bee.

9 To prove the toad did not refuse because it had grown wary of all food or was sated, another dragon-fly is offered.

10 The toad downs it just as it did the first dragon-fly. Demonstrably still hungry, it now knows good from bad.

The Apprentice Hunters

Like squirrels learning to open hazel-nuts, these adolescent lions are trying their best to bring down a large horned animal, in this case a brindled wildebeest. Just as soon as lion cubs can follow their mothers around, they watch her taking game. By 10 months, they are well practised at the art of stalking, keeping down wind and carrying out the flanking manœuvre so characteristic of lions. But for another year or so the actual capture and kill of game is left to their elders. Then, abruptly, young lions like the two-year-olds in these pictures find themselves out on their own. In this case the lioness, which has the wildebeest by the muzzle the way a cow-boy grasps a steer, stalked her prey expertly, charged from about 10 yards and correctly went for the head, fending off the horns with one paw. But though she clung like grim death, she lacked both the weight and the skill to throw her prey. Next time she will undoubtedly do better.

A PRIDE OF TWO-YEAR-OLD LIONS TAKES A FIRST CRACK AT BIG GAM

WHILE THE FIRST FEMALE HOLDS ON, A SECOND JOINS THE ATTACK AND HELPS TO BRING THE PREY DOWN. IN A STATE OF SHOCK, IT DOES NOT STRUGGL

148

ONE FEMALE HAS THE RIGHT IDEA, GRIMLY CLAWING THE BEAST'S MUZZLE WHILE HER BROTHER INEFFECTUALLY BITES AND PUSHES FROM BEHIND

SCANT HELP IS PROVIDED BY THE MALE, WHO, TRUE TO LION TRADITION, EATS HEARTILY BUT LEAVES THE HARD WORK OF KILLING TO FEMALES

7

Living Together

Some of man's most stirring human experiences, and many of his highest achievements, are due to his social nature—his urge and capacity for doing things and sharing experiences with other men. At the same time, and at first glance paradoxically, man's social attitudes include hostility, intolerance and antagonism. As his numbers increase and his control over his environment grows, these other characteristics become more and more dangerous until, today, they threaten mankind with self-destruction. Even if we were not interested in the social behaviour of animals for its own sake, our longing for happiness, our mere hope for survival, should encourage us to take a close look at the ways in which our social fellow animals deal with the very real problems of living together.

If we take the word in its widest sense, embracing all types of interaction between individuals of the same species, very few animals are not, at one time or another, "social". While the social nature of herds of African big game, of schools of fish, of flocks of migrating waders, of societies of termites, is self-evident, we might hesitate to call "social" the intricate interaction between the members of a breeding pair or between parents and offspring—and the fighting between rival males in spring might at first glance even seem to deserve the epithet anti-social. Yet, as we shall see, all these interactions have a great deal in common; all contribute to the success of the species, all depend on communication between individuals, and the methods used by different animals to achieve this communication, although they may appear widely varied, are basically the same.

The simplest aspect of social behaviour is herding, schooling or flocking—just being together. Yet we must not consider all gatherings of animals to be expressions of sociality. The clouds of insects that whirl around a lamp on a summer night may have been attracted individually to the light and may interact no more than snowflakes falling on the ground. For aggregations to be called social, the animals must at least move towards and remain with one another. Bees in a swarm, starlings in a flock, wildebeest in a herd, remain together wherever they go.

However, social animals do much more than merely stay together. They *do* things together; the activities of all members are jointly timed and orientated, and they do this too by influencing one another. A family of ducklings in the park goes through a common rhythm. Part of the day they all feed, keeping close together wherever they go. On other occasions they bathe together, and after a bath they swim to the shore together and spend half an hour or so preening, standing next to each other. Then they fall asleep, side by side.

But even this is not all. On many occasions there is a division of labour between the members of a group. This is seen in its most rigid form in the "castes" of social insects. In a beehive, there is a queen, there are thousands of workers, and at certain times of the year there are males or drones. Each of these castes has its own role in the hive. Even the jobs of the workers are divided up; depending on their age they will feed the brood or do the outside foraging or stand guard and repel strangers, while others take care of the ventilation of the hive.

There is also division of labour in more solitary animals, namely between male and female, and in the higher animals this applies not merely to the different roles in mating but also to different parental activities. For instance, the members of a pair of jewel-fish take turns in the guarding and guiding of their fry. Again, although a flock of geese has no single leader, all, and particularly the adult ganders, take their turn in sentinel duty. Among baboons the young males tend to stray from the main group and so spot an enemy first; their alarmed behaviour alerts the others, and in this way they too act as sentinels. In chimpanzees the old, experienced males lead the group and keep a sharp lookout at all times.

In short, social behaviour—the joint activities that make the community function—depends on various types of interaction among individuals, each playing its part in communication with others. For a full understanding of this, we must now ask the same questions about social interaction that we asked about the behaviour of an individual animal, namely: what is the survival value of social behaviour, how is it organized, how do social systems develop, and how have they taken shape in evolution?

Social interactions may be beneficial in many and often obvious ways. Clearly, no bisexual species could exist without intricate co-operation between male and female for the purpose of mating, and species in which the young receive parental care need close co-operation at least between parents and young. Living

RIDING HERD ON THE FRY

Certain cichlid fishes, like the jewel-fish shown here, watch over their young after hatching and keep them in a small tight school for safety. They do this by swimming in a conspicuous zigzag motion, which the young fry follow. When one parent arrives to relieve the other, there must be a way of changing guard, so that the young will not scatter or follow the other parent as it swims away. The lines in the drawing above show what happens. One parent comes rapidly in, in a straight line, and starts zigzagging as soon as it is in the school. Instantly the other parent darts away on a straight course, and the school is undisturbed.

in crowded conditions may have various advantages too. Social caterpillars keep each other warm and so speed up each other's development. The gulls of a breeding colony attack predators in force, and this concerted defence, quickly mounted as the birds alert each other by alarm calls, is much more successful than individual attacks. This success is not merely because the gulls nest close together but also because they nest at exactly the same time. Black-headed gulls that nest earlier or later than the bulk of the colony lose many more eggs and young to predators than those that lay in step with the majority. Even water fleas, or *Daphnia*, have been shown to profit from schooling: paradoxically some fish that live on them are distracted by their large numbers and gobble up fewer individuals in a dense *Daphnia* crowd than they do in a more scattered group. The advantage of social life is also striking in species that feed together: birds that feed socially find more food than each would on its own because they stimulate each other to feed, and a single bird will often attract others to abundant food sources when it finds them.

Since social life confers so many advantages, one might well ask why there are solitary animals at all. The answer is that solitariness can also be useful, though in a different way. Nature has designed very many ways to success, and solitariness is involved in some of them. For instance, most camouflaged animals live scattered. This has to do with the fact that many predators can find even the most skilfully camouflaged prey if they really turn their attention to it, and this they do only when there is promise of a rich reward—in other words, when they can find many of these animals in a short time. Thus, while large, strong species may profit from crowding by warding off a predator through massive attacks, small vulnerable species may be better off by living well spaced out. Conversely, most large predatory animals have their own special reasons for living alone—each of them needs a large stock of prey animals.

Solitariness, or living scattered, is ensured in many different ways. The most efficient of these is by fighting, and that is one of the reasons why so many animals fight regularly. Even social animals keep each other at a certain distance; they set a limit to their crowding. Starlings, crows and gulls often fight over food. Many higher animals are, at least in the reproductive season, territorial; in such species it is usually the males that drive off rival males from their chosen piece of ground. Thus even a "solitary" animal interacts with others at times and from this point of view must be called social.

In all these examples it is easy to see that the aggressor benefits when he wins—but unless a fight is even, there must also be a loser, and what advantage can there be in losing? The answer is that aggression pays only if you win, and if you face a superior opponent it is wiser to withdraw. A male of the territorial species has a better chance to produce offspring by moving to unoccupied territory than by wasting time and energy in hopeless battles with a superior rival. Success goes to the animal that knows when to flee as well as when to attack. Thus it is a finely balanced system of attack and fleeing behaviour rather than uninhibited aggressiveness that has survival value.

The many advantages of social interaction have led to the evolution of many different types of sociality in the animal world. Understanding them requires, as a first step, a knowledge of how their interactions are organized. To learn this we must obviously begin by studying the effect that one individual has on another. Of course, this study of animal communication involves that of individual behaviour, and the preceding chapters contain much that is relevant here too. But in social phenomena something new is added. In any communication system there is a transmitting, or signalling, party, and a receiving, or responding, party. Not only must we understand the behaviour of both the signaller and the reacting individual but we must also see how these behaviours fit so that co-operation is the result. When animals communicate with each other through behaviour, they are, as it were, "talking". This "language" of animals has been studied in many species. Compared with human speech it is very simple, but whereas our language is based mainly on sounds, animal communication is more varied and richer in that many other sensory channels can be involved—in fact any sense organ can be used for signalling purposes.

WE are only beginning to discover how many animals communicate with chemicals. A simple example is found among barnacles. These small sea animals, although they look very different from crayfish, are actually quite closely related to them. Like many marine creatures, they start life as free-floating larvae carried at will by the sea currents. Only when they grow older do they adopt a fixed, or "sessile", life, dropping to the bottom, growing shells and anchoring themselves to rocks or pilings or the bottoms of boats. They prefer to spend their sessile stage on or near old established barnacle beds—which is why we almost always find barnacles in clumps. And they locate existing beds by responding to "barnacle scent" given off by adult barnacles.

Scent is also widely used as a sexual attractant and has been thoroughly studied in certain moths like the silkworm moth and the gypsy moth. The females of these species have special glands which, as long as they are virgins, produce a chemical to which the males are highly sensitive. Some of these substances have now been chemically analysed and turn out to be relatively large molecules 15 to 25 times the weight of a carbon atom. They are known as social hormones, or pheromones. In addition to bringing the sexes together, pheromones play a part in mating behaviour and are also used by foraging ants to lay out chemical trails which their nest mates follow.

The sense of touch—mechanical contact—is also used by many animals for the reception of signals. After a ripe female stickleback has been lured into the nest by the male, she cannot spawn until the male stimulates her by rhythmic prodding of the base of her tail; when we prevent a male from touching her she will not spawn. An experimenter in Austria long ago demonstrated that a sexually mature snail can be made to go through all its complicated mating movements simply by touching it with a fine brush at exactly the places where a sexual partner would touch it.

The lateral lines of fishes, which are sensitive to water movements, often play a part in the fighting that results from the sexual rivalry of males. In a more or less balanced fight, the opponents may arrange themselves parallel to each other and by vigorous tail beats aim strong water currents at each other's sides. By thus giving a powerful stimulus to the lateral lines of his rival, a fish may, in effect, beat him without actually touching him.

Since we ourselves communicate mainly by sounds and visual signals, it is not surprising that these are the types of language which we have studied most intensively among animals. Many locusts, frogs, a few reptiles and almost all birds use a variety of sounds as signals. A regular, simple sound, repeated at intervals, is used by many social birds to ensure flock cohesion—this was recognized early by the famous novelist Selma Lagerlöf, who in her charming story of Nils Holgersson makes the travelling geese continuously call: "Here am

THE BARNACLE:
SOLITARY IN YOUTH,
GREGARIOUS IN AGE

Changing behaviour to meet the needs of a changing body is well illustrated by the acorn barnacle. The young larvae (shown above) are free-swimming, transparent, defenceless little things, and their greatest need is to become well scattered after birth. They accomplish this by drifting in the water, keeping afloat by swimming. As they grow older (centre) they drop to the bottom and develop the hard shells that will protect them later in life. At this stage their urge to live separately is reversed; they seek out colonies of other barnacles (below). This is useful since the presence of others indicates a favourable living spot. Existing colonies advertise their location by emitting chemical secretions that the young ones home on.

I—where are you?" The mating calls or songs of many animals attract prospective sex partners, as one can easily show by playing one of the commercially available gramophone records of frogs near a spawning area in spring. In birds, song usually serves the dual purpose of attracting females and repelling males. Since the songs of different species are usually very different, there is little danger of females being attracted to the wrong species.

Of all the signals used by animals, it is the visual ones which have been studied the most thoroughly. They include not only movements and postures but also the type of signal which we ourselves employ in such things as flags, traffic lights and navigation beacons. For instance, in many birds the males are much more brightly coloured than the females. While the females require camouflage as part of the protection of their brood, the males can afford to have these bright colours, and they use them in a bewildering variety of ways in courtship and in the equally vital business of threatening and driving away rivals. The postures they assume in courtship and threat are always well adapted to showing off the bright colours. Sometimes a male seems to be just one large flag. In more vulnerable species which have gone in for camouflage, the bright colours are more often kept concealed and are made visible only when they are required. In these cases effective signalling by colour depends on specialized behaviour as well. The European robin, for instance, is perfectly camouflaged on the back, but a male in a fighting mood puffs up his brick-red breast and presents this warning signal to his opponent. Male lizards of many species are brightly coloured on their underside but are very cryptic when viewed from above. In the breeding season, they stand sideways in front of a rival or a female, rearing up and at the same time compressing their bodies laterally so that a maximum of bright blue or red underside is shown off in a visual broadside. Similar displays of bright colour patterns have been developed in all animals that have good eyes, and are found not only in birds, reptiles, amphibians and fishes but also in tarantulas and jumping spiders, butterflies, dragon-flies and even ink-fish. Zoologists have long been aware of the bewildering variety of colour patterns displayed by such animals, but it is only through recent experimental studies that we are beginning to understand what the uses of all these patterns are. Of course, not every bright colour is used as a social signal; as we have already seen, many patterns are used to scare off predators. There are still others of whose exact function we simply have no idea. The field is wide open for further research.

WHAT is the nature of all these signals? What kinds of messages do they convey? This we can find out only through study of the way animals respond to them. What little we do know shows that as a rule the message is extremely simple. In many cases a signal does no more than any other external stimulus; it triggers off an immediate response. One alarm call given by a gull makes all the neighbours look around. Often a signal orientates the reacting animal at the same time. A mating call makes a female move towards the male; a hostile posture elicits withdrawal in a rival; the red patch on the bill tip of a herring-gull makes the chick peck at it and so reach the food presented by the parent. The dance of the honey-bees not only rouses the workers in the hives but also tells them the direction and distance of the food source, but this is unique among animals—a male woodpecker cannot send a female to his nest hole by pointing to it; he has to fly to the nest himself and then attract the female to it. The only birds that approach the bees in this respect are female ducks,

THE PROD THAT MAKES
THE STICKLEBACK SPAWN

Before she can release her eggs in the nest made for her by the male, the female stickleback needs the stimulation of a number of prods that the male gives with his snout to the base of her tail. At this stage, it is not the presence of the male that is important, but simply the stimulus that one prodding itself provides, which can be duplicated with a glass rod manipulated by a human investigator.

who incite their mates to attack strange males by pointing at them with their heads. Often the stimulation has to be repeated and its effects built up, so that the response comes after a certain delay. A female gull has to make her head-tossing movements repeatedly to make the male mount her; the male stickleback has to give the female a series of prods to make her spawn.

There are also signals that stop a response rather than elicit it. For instance, the first impulse among males of many territorial animals is to attack females as well as other males. In such species the females have special postures that identify them as female and appease the males. Gannets and many other birds do this by turning the head away; in many fish which threaten by raising all the fins the appeasement is done by flattening them. Conversely, the females are often afraid of males, and males tone down their initially hostile postures and combine them with very different ones which have a reassuring effect on the females. This is the function of facing away in black-headed gulls.

PRIMROSE

VIOLET

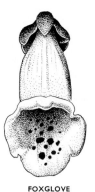

FOXGLOVE

LURES FOR POLLINATORS

The colours and fragrances of flowers entice pollinators, but many plants augment these lures with distinctive markings called honey guides. The primrose (top) has a star-shaped patch of yellow around its centre that attracts bees to the heart of the flower, where both the nectar and the pollen are. A series of stripes converges on the centre of a violet (middle), forming paths for insects to follow. The foxglove (bottom) marks the way differently; large dots near the lip of the blossom become smaller and denser towards the centre, leading a pollinator in.

Communication can be much more subtle than these examples suggest. Even in the simple case of a territorial male bird threatening off a neighbour, the signal he uses can vary over a wide range from weak to strong, depending on how deeply the intruder is penetrating his territory. A group of chimpanzees will watch the behaviour of their "wise old man" intently, and undoubtedly receive much information from him. When a mother hen pecks at food, the chick is not merely stimulated to feed but it may notice what kind of food the mother is pecking at and set out to find that food itself.

We even find signal systems that link different species which have entered into a mutually beneficial, or symbiotic, relationship. The colours and scents of flowers, for example, act as signals to their pollinators. In other instances, the signalling of one species may be to the disadvantage of a different species: the eye-spots on the wings of moths act as threat signals to some of their predators and cheat them out of a potentially good meal.

A great deal has been written about the question of what makes animals give their signals. It is easy to assume that a male bird attracting a female by his song is deliberately calling with the conscious purpose of influencing her to come to him. But words like "deliberate" and "conscious", referring as they do to subjective phenomena, lead us away from the more meaningful question: what *makes* the animal signal. Sometimes the signal may itself be a response to an outside stimulus—a woodpecker on its territory will reply to the drumming sound of its neighbour by drumming itself. Or internal conditions can be shown to play a part: cockerels can be induced to crow and to court hens prematurely by injections with male sex hormone.

As to what the animal does—its choice of a signal, so to speak—this, too, is beginning to be understood, thanks to some careful analysis of threat and courtship behaviour. For example, a threat posture is obviously triggered off by the appearance of an intruder, and it is, as we have seen in an earlier chapter, a product of a motivational conflict—the animal at one and the same time experiences the urge to fight and run away. Since it cannot do both of these things at the same time, it postures. It can do so in a variety of ways, some of them quite extraordinary. Sometimes it manages to combine both urges into a single gesture or attitude, just as a man will stand with fists clenched, but not daring to come forward and use them. Cichlid fishes do the same thing: they face each other aggressively, their tails lashing them boldly ahead while their pectoral fins just as strongly back-pedal to make sure that they stay where they are. In other cases a provoked animal will attack, but instead of attacking the source of its anger, perhaps a large and fearsome-looking opponent, it will attack a smaller or weaker bystander or even a stick or leaf on the ground —as you or I might, in frustrated anger, bang on the table with a fist. Under extreme provocation, an animal may even make movements that have no direct relationship to threats and fighting at all. Male starlings will deal with the tense situation of facing each other near a nest hole by preening their plumage assiduously between bouts of actual fighting. There can be little doubt that many if not most signalling movements have their origin in such motivational conflicts; how and when they have acquired signal function is an evolutionary question to which we shall presently return.

Closely tied to threat signals are the appeasement and reassuring postures. These too are the result of a motivational conflict, but they need not involve aggression, though they do involve fear. A kittiwake gull that is intimidated and yet unwilling to retreat from its nest site or its mate turns its face away. This facing away is in a sense a symbolic fleeing, yet the gull does not really flee. In turning away it flashes a signal which says "I am fleeing", and this reduces the aggressiveness of the opponent.

With courtship the situation is often even more intricate. Admittedly some types of courtship are very simple. The males of frogs and toads just croak; this attracts the females, and as soon as a female comes within reach of a male he clasps her. He even clasps other males, but is promptly discouraged by another signal: an assaulted male simply utters a short protesting grunt and this wards off the assailant. Much more elaborate courtships are found in species where one partner has to be persuaded *not* to do something that would interfere with mating. Some male spiders have to go through complicated antics to make sure that the female of their choice does not confuse them with prey and eat them. Among territorial animals, where aggression and withdrawal from rivals is vital for the purpose of spacing out, the situation may be particularly confusing, since the hoped-for partner may not make the proper sexual response at all but instead may either attack or run away and so give the same stimuli as a territorial opponent. Sometimes all three reactions are blended into a signal closely resembling the threat posture but whose aggressive overtones are blunted by accompanying postures of reassurance or appeasement. These postures are seen repeated in species that have a bethrothal period during which they do not yet mate but instead spend some time getting to know each other as individuals. As their familiarity with one another increases, the complex courtship signals gradually subside, although they may flare up again briefly in a "meeting ceremony" each time the partners reunite.

Thus the first probes into this fascinating field have already led to a revelation: what looks like an elaborate "language" is really a system of rather simple messages. Like weeping or smiling in man, these both express and induce a mood or emotional state.

Our knowledge of animal communication would remain incomplete if we failed to study the ways in which social groupings originate and grow. It seems that there are three main types of development. Some communities form by individuals coming together; a male and a female, at first both solitary, join. This, as we have seen, may often be a cumbersome, difficult process. The male, however much attracted to the female, may attack her at first, and the female may flee. But each partner will express its conflict by appeasement and reassurance signals, and the difficulty may be overcome. A second type of community is formed by a process of "differentiation"; the embryo is originally just a part of the mother but gradually acquires individuality. This process goes even further in the formation of the "states" of bumble-bees or social wasps, which are the offspring of one single queen. A third method is found in the large communities of honey-bees and termites. These undergo from time to time a process called "sociotomy". Sociotomy occurs when the community splits up in two roughly equivalent communities.

This is a very brief and simplified account of the kinds of social groupings that are formed, and we must be equally brief now about how the animals that form them acquire the ability to do so. In short, is social behaviour innate or learned? Generally speaking, signalling behaviour is innate (although, as we have seen, the songs of chaffinches and some other birds are partly learned), whereas the responses to the signals, though often innate, are in many animals improved by learning.

ARE there any useful lessons in this for men? It is, of course, of the greatest importance to know the extent to which the social environment can mould social responses. This is perhaps the most basic sociological problem facing us in our own species. Human beings, let us face it, are very aggressive, dangerously so since we have developed the means of genocide without developing efficient inhibitions to keep ourselves in check. And this brings us to the question: What can animal behaviour studies teach us about ourselves? Ultimately, of course, we can base conclusions about our own species only on investigations of human behaviour—no animal study can be a full substitute. But we can at least apply to ourselves the methods that are proving fruitful with animal behaviour; we can also perhaps make some inspired guesses. It is not known at the moment whether or not our aggressiveness has an innate basis—or, looking at it from the other side, whether educational methods could be found to produce non-aggressive men. The best present guess of comparative behaviour students is that this will not be possible; there are signs that man is inherently equipped with both individual and group aggression. Even if it were possible to eliminate aggression, it seems very likely that the resulting gentle humans would have lost other very valuable attributes as well. There are undoubted links between aggression and the motives that drive us into activities and attitudes which are considered desirable. Even friendship itself may well be a concomitant of group aggression—shared hostility forges powerful links between individuals. At any rate, it appears that for the foreseeable future we shall have to live with our aggressive tendencies and it behoves us to try to curb them in the best possible ways. Here we can learn a great deal from animal studies. We can investigate how education can at least avoid increasing aggressiveness, as it may well be doing today in competitive societies. We can teach sensitivity and imaginativeness and compassion for the victims of aggression; this is urgent because our long-range weapons allow us to kill and wound at a distance where the natural appeasement behaviour of our fellow men cannot be seen or heard. We can try to discover the best ways to deflect and sublimate our aggression—by finding symbolic sticks to attack, tables to bang or, better yet, by conquering nature as in the conquest of space or in some gigantic power or irrigation project. In these and other ways the study of the social behaviour of animals may well help us to serve—and possibly save—ourselves, and thus it may ultimately emerge as the most important science of all.

AT NIGHT A MALE TOAD CALLS TO A FEMALE WITH A CROAK WHICH SWELLS HIS THROAT, FORMING A PALE BEACON TO HELP HER TO FIND HER WAY

Animal Communication

In order to co-operate, animals must be able to communicate. They do this in a baffling number of ways, using any and all of their sense organs. Compared to human speech, their language is simple —the difference between a growl and an articulated word. Yet, whatever the method, whether the communicants be a pair of mating toads or a town of prairie dogs, they manage to be understood.

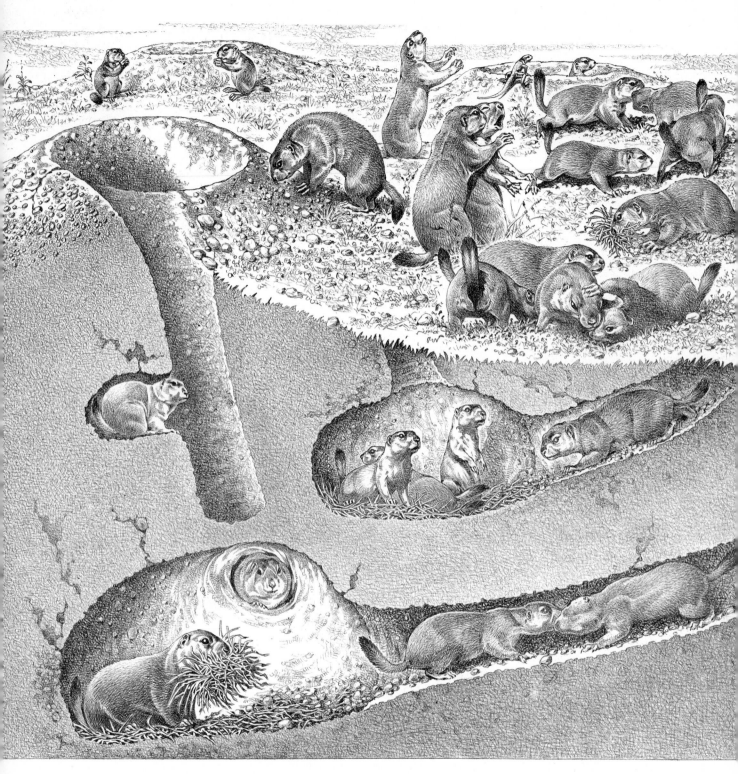

A PRAIRIE DOG TOWN, with its complex social structure, depends on communication of several kinds between its members: scent, vision, hearing and touch. The basic social unit is the coterie, comprising usually one or two adult males, two or more adult females, several babies and a few juveniles. Each coterie defends its territory against the encroachment of its neighbours, thus maintaining a balance between available food and population. In order to keep out trespassers, prairie dogs must be able to recognize each other. They can do this by sight, but they confirm recognition by exchanging a kiss (8), (10), (12), (14). The male standing in the open on its hind

feet and barking (5) is proclaiming territorial sovereignty. Adjacent coteries, though always squabbling over boundaries, co-operate by warning each other with a different bark when danger threatens. Prairie dogs feed (1) only during the day, subsisting mainly on grasses, roots and small seeds. Members of a new litter (11) remain in the nest. Prairie dog architecture follows a pattern. The earth piled up and pounded hard around the entrance (4) forms a dike against flash floods. Some three feet underground may be a guard room (2), to which the animals retreat when threatened. The nest itself (3), kept lined with grass, is usually found at the far end of a tunnel. Grooming,

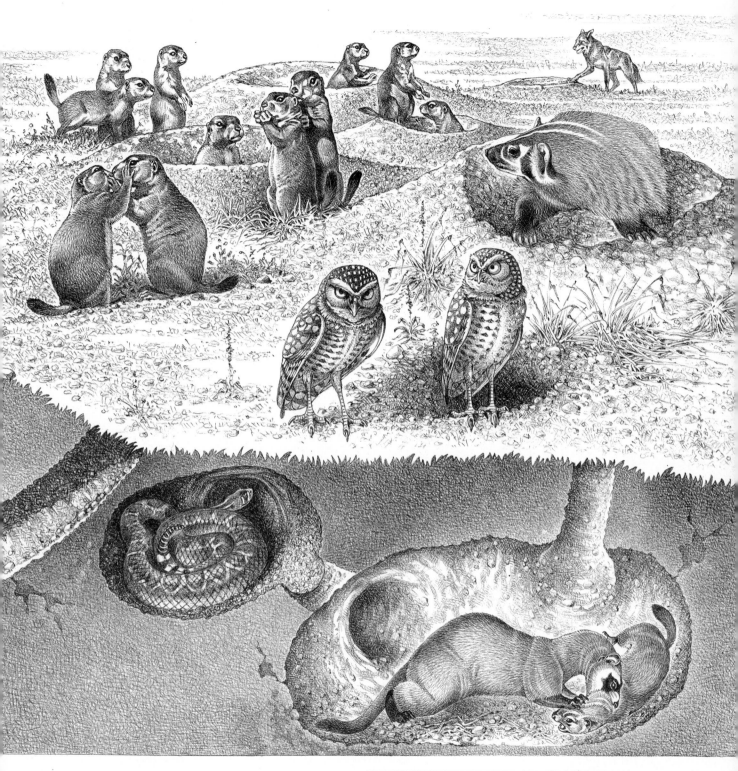

carried on only between members of the same coterie (7), (17), is another example of social behaviour. Three pups (13) poke heads out of a burrow showing the curiosity which is sometimes their undoing. Vacated tunnels may be inhabited by burrowing owls (18) and diamond-backed rattlesnakes (15), neither of which poses much threat to grown prairie dogs—nor does the western collared lizard (6), another visitor. However, the badger (19) and the black-footed ferret (20) are deadly threats—far more so than the coyote, which is being carefully watched by two adults (16), since the coyote can neither dig like the badger nor enter prairie dog tunnels like the ferret.

GREYLAG GOOSE—AT EASE

Postures and Patterns

Although speech is—to humans—obviously the best way to communicate, we often forget how expressive our smiles, tears, attitudes of body and manual gestures can be. A man, if hard put to it, can get along quite well without talking. Similarly, many animals are capable of conveying a remarkable

ATTITUDE OF ALARM

THREATENING AT A DISTANCE

ALL-OUT ATTACK

STRONG CONFLICT BETWEEN AGGRESSION AND FEAR

WEAK CONFLICT BETWEEN AGGRESSION AND FEAR

DEFENSIVE

INFERIORITY

TIMID SOCIAL APPROACH

APPROACH TO PROSPECTIVE MATE

amount of information to their fellows without uttering a sound. The greylag goose at the left, although it does call on occasion to show anger, depends almost entirely on posture to express itself. And the small fresh-water fish below, a member of the cichlid family, not only changes the position of its fins to express various emotions but actually changes its colour and pattern as well. It does this by expanding and contracting specially adapted red and black colour cells in its skin. Communication is particularly important for cichlids, which spawn in pairs and form strong family bonds.

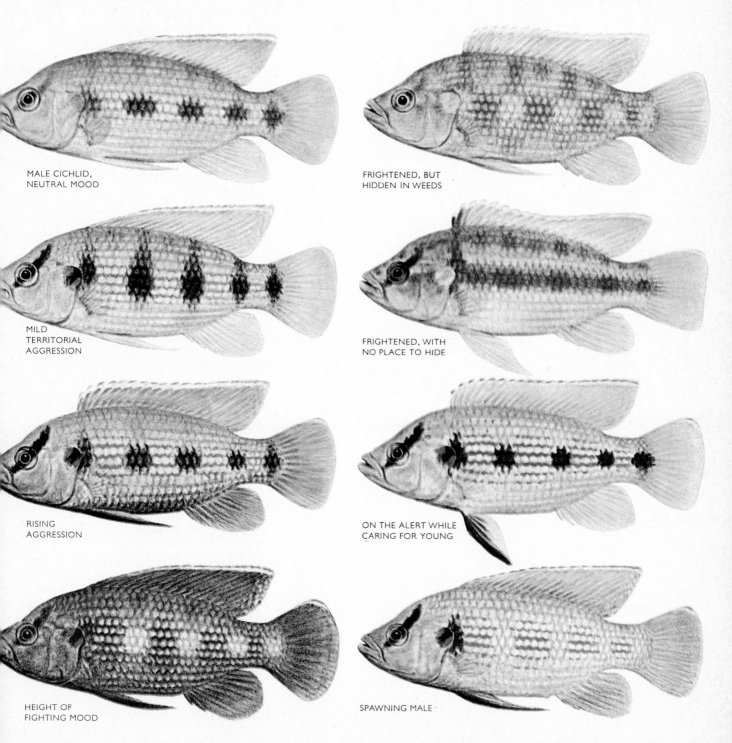

MALE CICHLID,
NEUTRAL MOOD

FRIGHTENED, BUT
HIDDEN IN WEEDS

MILD
TERRITORIAL
AGGRESSION

FRIGHTENED, WITH
NO PLACE TO HIDE

RISING
AGGRESSION

ON THE ALERT WHILE
CARING FOR YOUNG

HEIGHT OF
FIGHTING MOOD

SPAWNING MALE

NORMAL SHAPE OF A BELUGA'S FOREHEAD, WHEN NOT MAKING NOISE, IS SHOWN ABOVE—ROUND AND SLOPING DIRECTLY TO THE UPPER JAW

Communicating under Water

The world beneath the surface of the sea is not silent, as was once thought, but rather a cacophony of chirps, whistles and moans—much of it beyond the limits of the human ear. Down there, where sound waves travel faster and farther than they do in air, and where the light is poor and the visibility often nil, animals rely increasingly on sound as their need for communication increases. Fishes, for example, are relatively stupid and communicate with each other only slightly, if at all. They "hear" through their bodies, have little sense of the direction of a sound, and most of them are

WHEN MAKING A NOISE, IT CONTRACTS THE MUSCLES ABOVE ITS JAW AND BULGES OUT THE UPPER PART OF ITS HEAD INTO A SOUND CHAMBER

silent. The cetaceans—the whales, porpoises and dolphins—on the other hand, are highly intelligent and lead complex social lives. Being mammals, their ears are basically similar to ours but their hearing is far keener. Their ability to determine the position of an object, such as a reef, without being able to see it—as a bat does, by echo location—is extraordinary. They communicate with each other constantly and are capable of a wide variety of sounds. The champion conversationalist (*above*) is the beluga, or white whale— long known to British sailors as the "sea canary".

Signals and Responses

Though the language of the higher species can be immensely complex, much of the communication that takes place in the animal kingdom is very simple and direct. This is not surprising when one considers that the ability to think is rare among animals, and that most of their actions take place automatically. It is so with the amoeba and, to a lesser degree, it is so with man. Prick a *Homo sapiens* with a pin and he jumps. Communication need be no more complicated than that. Thus, for the male fiddler-crab at the left any mate will do, just so long as she is a female of the same species. The male, stimulated by an inner sexual urge, automatically begins to wave its claw, its most distinguishing feature, and the female, seeing it, automatically approaches.

When a little bird feels hungry, it gapes. That is the only language it knows—and all it need know at that stage of its development. Responding automatically to the target presented, the parent begins to stuff it with food, just as its parents before it responded to a like target, for the best target gets the most food and is most likely to reproduce itself. This selection process may well explain a curious but entirely logical parallel development of mouth spots in the young of certain parasitic species, like the widow-bird, who lay their eggs in the nests of other species. If the put-upon parents of these other species depend on spots to stimulate them to feed their young, obviously the young widow-birds will need mouth spots too. And they have them!

TO SUMMON A MATE, a male fiddler-crab begins to wave a claw (*top*). Its motions become more frantic (*middle photos*) as it senses a responding female. She prepares (*bottom*) to follow the male home.

MOUTH AGAPE, an infant parrot-finch displays four brilliant metal-coloured spots around its mouth, which trigger a feeding response in its parents. These spots will disappear after about five or six weeks.

The Language of Action

In the same way that people who speak different languages must communicate in crude signs, animals belonging to different species use the most blatant shows to make themselves understood. For the most part, the only message that one animal need pass to one of another species is a warning to stay out of its way or to keep out of its private territory. That is just what the belligerent blue jay is conveying to the great horned owl in the series of pictures below.

Normally such a threat is capable of being backed up with punishing action should it go unheeded—the whir of a rattlesnake and the growl of a dog are examples. However, in the situation below it is

FINDING A GREAT HORNED OWL NEAR ITS NEST, AN ENRAGED BLUE JAY DARTS TO ATTACK.   BUFFETING THE OWL SMARTLY WITH ITS WINGS,

fairly obvious that the much smaller jay could do no real harm to the immensely stronger owl. In fact, it is the owl, a predator used to feeding on songbirds, that is equipped to do serious damage to the jay. It is here that a breakdown in communication works to the advantage of the jay. The owl, having no natural enemy, has evolved no efficient reply to an attack. The jay's brazen behaviour confuses it and momentarily short-circuits the owl's normal predatory response to an animal smaller than itself. Without being able to understand what is happening, the owl grows uneasy. If it is bothered enough by the jay, it will retire, content to seek game which behaves the way game should, by running away.

THE JAY APPEARS TO LAND FOR AN INSTANT.   MAKING GOOD ITS ESCAPE, THE JAY TAKES OFF AGAIN AS THE BEWILDERED OWL DUCKS

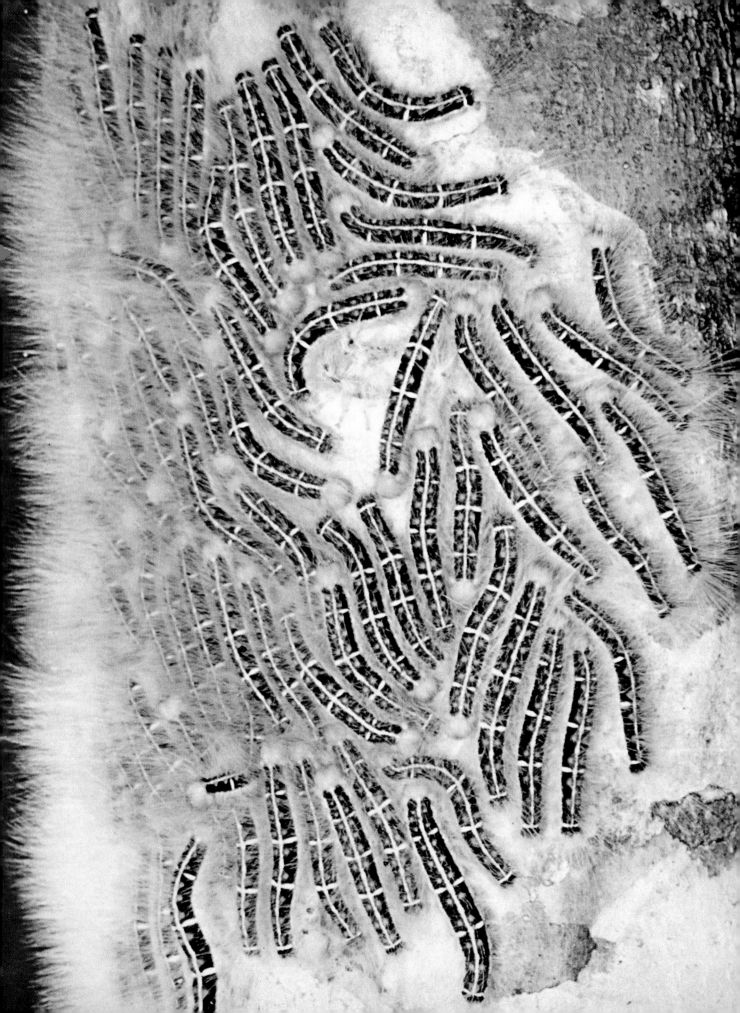

8

The Evolution
of Behaviour

THE picture that emerges as more and more workers join forces in penetrating the intricacies of animal behaviour is one of an almost endless variety of ways to survival. The basic units, such as sensory, nerve, muscle and gland cells, which work in much the same way throughout large groups of the animal kingdom, are integrated into immensely complex systems, each unique for a species, each efficiently meeting the demands of a hostile world in its own way. The spectrum of behavioural variety found among the multitude of animal types is at least as rich as that of size, shape and colour.

In the preceding chapters I have simply stated this as a fact. But our inquiry cannot stop here; we must now try to discover how this efficiency and this variety have come about.

No informed persons doubt any more that the many animal types that inhabit the earth today are the results of a long process of evolution. To understand how this evolution has happened is one of the major tasks of biology. The course which evolution must have taken has been deduced mainly from the study of fossils. The mechanisms by which it has been, and is still being, controlled are inferred from a wealth of evidence gathered by geneticists, taxonomists, anatomists, ecologists and other biologists. Modern evolutionary theory, which is the product of their combined efforts, and which is a refinement, an elaboration and extension of Darwin's theory of natural selection, is a superb synthesis and may be summarized as follows.

The transfer, from parents to offspring, of the genetic instructions that control the development of each new individual is normally—but not always—achieved with faultless precision by the genes of the sex cells. However, there are cases where this transmission is not exact, and offspring receive slightly different genes from those the parents originally had. This happens rarely with any particular gene, but since each species has numerous genes and since many populations are large, and also because any changes that do occur in the genes are followed by other processes such as recombination in later generations, individuals within a population of any species vary considerably—in fact it is almost true to say that no two individuals are exactly alike genetically. If this is so, it follows that different individuals cannot be equally well equipped for survival and that the pressures of the environment will slowly but inexorably discriminate against the less fit types. Provided genetic variability is continuously created and maintained (as we know it is), this process of natural selection forces all species to adapt themselves to their environments. Because the environments keep changing, and species keep expanding their range and invading new habitats, the process is endless and species keep evolving. On the other hand, genetic variability means that a well-adapted species is in constant danger of deterioration; selection keeps such a species "on its toes"—it stabilizes successful types. The selection pressures are of almost endless variety and even include one for genetic variability itself, so that the two processes of variation and selection interact continuously.

THIS, in a very small nutshell, is the essence of modern evolutionary theory. Fossils provide the student of animal structure with a kind of direct, although very fragmentary, historical documentation. Unfortunately, fossils do not "behave", and so we have no direct knowledge of the course behavioural evolution has followed in the past. Yet there is a great deal of indirect evidence which allows us to say something about the way behaviour has evolved. We begin to have an inkling of how mutation and selection act on behaviour, and to see how their combined action produces both increased variety and efficiency.

Since any animal does have a certain shape and certain kinds of specialized organs and equipment, one might be excused for thinking that it develops its characteristic behaviour through a trial-and-error process of finding out what it can best do with that equipment. In this sense one might say that a fish learns to swim by discovering that fins are structurally better for swimming than for walking. Similarly, one might suppose that adaptation to the environment could come about as the animal experimented with various kinds of behaviour until it hit on the one which best suited its surroundings—learning to swim would obviously be useful to an animal that lived in the water, for example.

If this were all there was to it, behavioural evolution would offer no particular problems. Being dependent on structure and environment, behaviour would be able to express itself only indirectly in ways that structure and environment "permitted". However, that is by no means the whole story. Behaviour is often expressed directly—species that appear to be structurally similar and that live in the same environment do act differently. This means that they *are* different in some way, and the difference lies in their genes—not genes for blue eyes or long legs, but genes for behaviour: genes for tameness, aggressiveness, vigour in courtship, ability to learn a maze, and a host of other things that have no apparent connection with the animal's shape or its environment at all.

It is true that in some cases a behavioural difference between species is the direct product of the environment. Certain ducks offer a fascinating example of this. When male mallards or male pintails are raised with their own kind, they will mate only with females of their own kind. But if male mallards are raised from birth with pintails, they will try to mate with pintails. Similarly, male pintails raised with mallards will try to mate with them instead of their own species. This shows that male mallards and male pintails do not differ innately in mate selection; the fact that both normally choose females of their own species merely reflects a difference in the social environment in which they grow up. Astonishingly enough, however, this is not the case with the females of these two species. Even when raised with the wrong species, they will accept only males of their own species as sexual partners. This is the expression of a true difference between female pintails and mallards, a difference that is just as real and just as constant as the differences in the shapes of their bills or the colours of their feathers.

Despite the example of the ducks and of several others that might be given, the vast majority of behaviour patterns cannot be accounted for by environment or structure alone. The behavioural uniqueness of a species is mainly an expression of its genetic uniqueness. This has long been suspected by naturalists. Now, studies of behaviour genetics are beginning to confirm it. In a number of cross-breeding experiments between different species or between different strains of the same species, many behavioural characteristics—like the above-mentioned gentleness and aggressivenesss—have been found to be inherited in the same way as structural characteristics.

An interesting cross-breeding experiment between two species of love-birds was conducted by William C. Dilger of Cornell University. One of these species has the peculiar habit of cutting up strips of leaf or bark for its nest and then tucking them in the feathers of its rump, and in that way carrying them to the nest site. The other species carries its material in its bill. The hybrids between these two species carried material both ways. They started off by carrying most of it tucked in the rump feathers. But this was less efficient than transportation by bill; it kept falling out, and they subsequently learned to use their bills more and more. Even then, however, they still began by ruffling up their rump plumage and attempting to tuck.

EVEN a single mutation can alter behaviour. This has been shown of the courtship behaviour of the fruit-fly *Drosophila melanogaster*. A normal male fruit-fly stimulates the female by vibrating its wings rapidly while facing her. These vibrations come in short bursts separated by intervals of quiet, and after a number of bursts the male mounts and mates. However, there is a type of so-called "yellow mutant" fly which differs from the normal type in only one genetic factor. The yellow males vibrate less and make fewer attempts at copulation than the normal males.

Although behaviour genetics is still in its infancy, it is already clear that a great many behaviour characteristics are influenced by genetic change and that genetic variability between species and populations is as large for behaviour characters as it is for structural characters. It is even very likely that behaviour differences between individuals of the same population are at least in part

SPINES FOR SURVIVAL

Although all sticklebacks have sharp spines on their backs, these vary greatly in size, and the variations go hand in hand with differences in behaviour. The drawing above shows a male of the 10-spined variety in the background. Its spines are small and offer little protection against predatory fish. As a result, it lurks in the weeds and is drably coloured even during the breeding season. By contrast, those of the three-spined variety (foreground) are much longer; they enable their owners not only to live bolder lives but also to sport much brighter colours. To pike (below) and other predatory fish, they are like animated pincushions and are seldom molested. When they are, they are usually spat out unhurt.

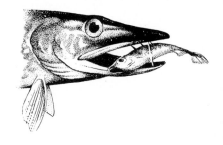

genetically determined. Since behaviour contributes so much to the success of animals, this genetic variability makes it possible for the process of natural selection to favour, over long periods of time, the best-adapted types.

To find out what natural selection has achieved, it would of course be best to imitate it—in other words to do the selecting ourselves and see whether evolution in the expected direction occurs. This is, of course, what man has done through his deliberate breeding to improve the stock of domesticated animals. But this vast experiment has been concerned mainly with form, size and colour, and has not given much information about the evolution of behaviour. Yet we have undoubtedly selected for such things as tameness and fast and promiscuous mating in our breeding stocks of most domestic animals. This is a bit hard to demonstrate in the case of such animals as the domestic cow and horse, since their wild ancestors are no longer around for comparison. However, the ancestor of the domestic goose, the greylag goose, is still with us. This bird is strictly monogamous—so much so that widowers often fail to re-mate—but farmyard ganders, after a few thousand years of selective breeding, are true Casanovas.

The best records have been obtained in experiments deliberately designed for the study of behaviour evolution. Naturally, such experiments are done with animals in which the generations follow each other in quick succession, so that one single worker can study many generations. Not surprisingly, it is again the fruit-fly, which can produce many generations in a year, that has been used. A recent experiment was designed to test whether selection could increase the tendency of closely related strains to mate only within their own strain. Two strains were taken which, though they did interbreed quite readily in the natural state, did not do so indiscriminately; at the start of the experiment they both preferred their own kind, though only slightly. Equal numbers of both sexes of both strains were allowed to mix and to mate. Cross-breeding individuals were selected against by killing all their hybrid offspring, so that they could not contribute to later generations. Pure offspring of both strains—which of course were the product of like having mated with like—were again mixed and allowed to mate, and the hybrid offspring of this generation eliminated in turn. This was done for three years, by which time the 40th generation had emerged. This admittedly very severe anti-hybrid selection over a mere 40 generations had a marked effect. The males of both strains of the last generation mated preponderately with females of their own strain, and females courted by the wrong males refused them much more consistently than females of the first generation had done. Both evolutionary changes produced a greatly increased degree of sexual isolation between the strains. Of course this experiment does not prove that this is how selection *has* produced sexual isolation, but it shows that it *can* do so.

IN addition to applying a known selection pressure and seeing what happens, we can also attack the problem from the other side. If natural selection has been responsible for the evolution of the adaptedness of behaviour in an animal, then the way that animal is behaving at this moment must obviously contribute to its survival. This is why studies of the survival value of behaviour are not only important in their own right but are also required for an understanding of evolution.

The first step is to find out whether or not a given behaviour contributes to success, and which selection pressure it meets. Sometimes this can be decided by close observation, by putting two and two together. For instance, once we know that a bird requires the heat insulation provided by the air captured in its plumage and that it responds to cold weather by fluffing its plumage and so enlarging the air layer, we can be sure that plumage fluffing is useful as a defence against cold. In other cases, experiments are required. Until it had been shown that insect-eating birds find counter-shaded caterpillars more readily when they are sitting in the "wrong" position (which makes them conspicuous among flat leaves), we could not be sure that the posture of the caterpillars was part of their defence against such predators. Similarly, we would not have an inkling of the function of synchronized breeding of gulls if we had not found that early and late broods suffer more from predators than the majority raised in the middle of the breeding season.

The evidence, gradually being accumulated through such studies of survival value, is still rather patchy. Yet a very rich picture begins to emerge already, one of undreamed-of variety of behavioural adaptation, meeting the multitude of environmental pressures in many different ways and in astonishing detail.

THE INTERPLAY BETWEEN BODY AND BEHAVIOUR

A special shape or colour is often useless without appropriate behaviour. The colouring of the eyed hawk-moth caterpillar is such that when it hangs from the underside of a twig, the light coming from above gives it a uniform shade and renders it extremely inconspicuous to hungry birds (above). But if turned over, the unfortunate caterpillar immediately becomes visible (below), for its back now looks much too bright and its underside too dark. Although it does not "know" this, it nevertheless hastens to get back under the twig, since its normal behaviour is to remain in an upside-down position.

To take one particular example, the spacing out of the members of a number of species is ensured by a variety of behaviour patterns. These "dispersion mechanisms" reduce competition to a minimum. Perhaps the simplest way to disperse is just to drift aimlessly about for a while, carried and scattered by the wind or water until the time for settling has arrived. The larvae of many marine animals, such as shellfish, starfish and crabs, do this; after a few days, weeks or even months of floating life they change their behaviour, sink to the bottom and settle down. Many kinds of caterpillars would lose the effectiveness of their natural camouflage and become dangerously conspicuous if they stayed together in large groups. To prevent this, the moths of some species scatter their eggs when they lay them. However, the peppered moth, whose larvae also must live scattered if their camouflage is to be effective, lays her eggs in a tight cluster. It is up to the larvae themselves to do something about this, and as soon as they emerge from the eggs, each tiny caterpillar climbs to the top of the bush, spins a gossamer thread and sails away on the wind.

Still other camouflaged caterpillars—and many higher animals also—rely on their own powers of locomotion and move away from others of their kind. The females of some parasitic wasps distribute their kind by refusing to lay their eggs in an already occupied host. Swarming bees move away as a group; when offered empty hives at different distances from their starting point, they avoid those less than a couple of hundred yards away. Territorial animals apply an even better method; they avoid competition with each other as long as they have not found a suitable site, but once they have settled, they drive off newcomers. Among certain ducks, a male that has already mated and has a nesting female of its own on hand will greet any other female that wanders into the area with rough attempts to mate, unsoftened by any of the courtship preliminaries that female ducks require. This makes the females avoid occupied areas and has the effect of spacing out the nests. Dragon-flies do the same thing, but in an even cruder way. Males try to mate with any intruder, male or female, and while females may accept them, assaulted males move away.

Most of our understanding of the powers of natural selection we owe to the field biologists, who study animal behaviour in the natural environment. It is the natural habitat which has exerted and is exerting the pressures to which animals are adapted and it is therefore not surprising that an increasing amount of behaviour research is done in the field.

However, in order to judge whether or not the truly marvellous refinement of adaptedness can be due to selection, we have to do more than show that an animal would have less chance of survival if it would fail to show a given behaviour altogether—we have to check whether even small deviations from the normal behaviour are penalized. This has as yet been done rarely. For certain structural properties, such as the camouflaged twig-like form of some caterpillars and the eye-spots of moths, amazingly slight deviations have been shown to be indeed harmful. Similarly, many behaviour patterns are obviously perfect or very nearly so. For instance, the immobility of many camouflaged moths by day could hardly be improved on; the homing ability of bees and wasps based on their recognition of landmarks could not be better. But when we explore this problem of perfection a little further, we soon discover that a certain behaviour does not always seem to be the best possible solution to the survival problem. A crow does occasionally break through the defences of a gull colony and grab an egg; a male gannet often pecks a female so ferociously that she leaves him. This suggests that the gulls' defences could be better and that the gannet's mating behaviour is ill-adapted. But a closer study of such examples often shows that an improvement in one respect would be harmful in another context. Crows are dangerous to adult gulls as well as to their eggs, and adult gulls therefore must avoid being over-aggressive. The male gannet has to be aggressive to secure a breeding site, for without one it just cannot hope to raise offspring. Our first impression of inefficiency was therefore due to the narrow scope of our study. It is over-all efficiency that is promoted by selection. Selection cannot be expected to influence single characters without any regard for harmful side effects, but must lead to compromise solutions. Numerous examples of this are known both in the structure and in the behaviour of animals. The foot of a goose is not ideal for either swimming or walking, but it does both reasonably well. Although the empty egg-shell on the rim of a gull's nest endangers the brood by its conspicuousness, it is not removed promptly. This may seem less than perfect—but as long as a chick is still wet it is extremely vulnerable to predation and the parent gull cannot remove the shell without exposing the chick. It usually compromises by leaving the shell where it is until the chick has dried.

WE find imperfection of another type in defences against predators and in similar behaviour that has to keep pace with other species. No prey species has a perfect defence against its predators—as the prey improves its defences, the predator steps up the efficiency of its attack. A shrimp camouflages itself well by digging into the sand, but a cuttle-fish can crack its defence by its trick of blowing the sand away. Man has created many changes in the environment of animals which evolution, slow as it is, has not yet been able to cope with. For instance, the wholesale drainage of marshes in Western Europe has forced the black-headed gull to move to sand dunes, which are less good as a breeding habitat. For one thing, they suffer at times heavy depredations from foxes, which in the dunes are not handicapped by water as they would be in a marsh.

Finally, a behaviour pattern may be imperfect because a species may have committed itself too deeply to one particular method of doing things. The drinking movements of pigeons, which, almost unique among birds, pump water through their bills, would seem to be more efficient than the scooping of other birds, yet scooping persists among most other species. Why? It may be simply that a bird cannot switch to pumping without first going through an inefficient stage, and this is prevented by selection.

Imperfection therefore is often apparent rather than real, or it may be inevitable; either way, it is not *per se* an argument against natural selection. But the numerous examples of behaviour which by painstaking studies have been shown to be well adapted are positive demonstrations of the power of natural selection—there just is no other plausible explanation.

So far we have been considering the evolution of the last stages of perfection of behaviour, and, while we may have been convinced that selection leads to improvement, we are left with one important question: how have these wonders of efficiency originated in the first place? How, in the course of evolution, do "novel" characters appear? How did it happen that pigeons and their relatives began to drink by pumping water through their bills instead of scooping it up? How did birds begin to incubate their eggs?

UNFORTUNATELY, we know next to nothing about these matters. But for one class of behaviour we do have at least a well-established theory, namely for the signalling movements of higher animals, particularly those used in threat and courtship. As we have seen, these signals can often be recognized as the outcome of a motivational conflict—between attack and escape in threat situations, and between these two and sexual behaviour during courtship. Thus, male ducks make preening movements when courting females. However, they do not preen in quite the same way as when they are really trying to smooth their feathers. Instead of preening *any* part of the plumage, they confine their preening to the wing, and often just one part of the wing, usually a brightly coloured part. One duck in particular, the male mandarin, has among its wing feathers one that is greatly enlarged; it stands out like a huge orange flame among the smaller dark-green feathers, and it is this flag that the male touches in courtship. But its act is so far removed from the original preening gesture that it is only by comparison with other species of ducks that its origin can be recognized.

This is not the only case. Many movements, like preening, have taken on another function in addition to their original one. And the direction in which they have gone seems to have been largely determined by the sense organs of the recipient. In other words, the signals themselves have developed according to whatever provided the strongest stimulus for the receiving animal. Thus, animals which rely principally on eyesight also rely mainly on visual signals. These are usually exaggerated movements, distortions, we might almost say, of other more natural movements. They may take the form of a sudden and dramatic start and stop of some action, a rhythmic repetition of it or even the development of brightly coloured patches that the movement reveals.

All this, although primarily behavioural, might be compared to the physical development of an organ towards a new function. The claw of a lobster, for example, is now used as a tool for the crushing of hard food, although it was originally a walking leg.

Another requirement that signals have met is that of distinctiveness. No signal can be effective if it can be confused with another serving a different purpose—in mating, confusion could have particularly serious consequences for the perpetuation of the species, and so mating signals are particularly distinctive. Signals must not only be distinct from one another within the same species in order to avoid incorrect responses but they have also become distinct from the corresponding signals of closely related species, which tends to reduce the risk of hybridization.

If the comparative study of signal movements seems to show us how in gen-

SHELDUCK

MALLARD

GARGANEY

MANDARIN

THE EVOLUTION OF
A COURTSHIP GESTURE

The gradual evolution away from a recognizable preening gesture to something almost entirely symbolic may be traced in the behaviour of these four ducks. A male bird courting a female is in a conflict situation, and he cannot help making a "nervous movement". Thus, courting drakes preen their feathers. These movements have evolved into conspicuous signals which are typical of each species. The shelduck vigorously works over the shaft of its feathery wing. The mallard raises its wing to reveal a bright patch beneath and preens that. The garganey makes slight preening gestures at the blue front of the wing, and the mandarin duck gives a merely symbolic touch to one very large and bright feather—a movement no longer recognizable as preening.

eral "novel" characters originate, it also shows that these are not really novel at all, but derived from existing characters. It is we who are inclined to call them novel, to an increasing degree as selection modifies them more. A novel signal may also develop from the fusion of two known movements. For instance, the courtship dance of a male three-spined stickleback consists of a series of distinct zig-zag jumps with pauses between successive zig-zags. There is suggestive evidence that the "zag", which is a quick, abruptly stopping jump towards the female, is an incipient attacking movement, and that the "zig", usually away from her, is the beginning of the movement to leading her to the nest. Each zig-zag in the courtship chain is now a distinct unity with staccato qualities, and it is rhythmically repeated. It shows the female not only this striking movement but also shows off the male's brilliant colours. Experiments with dummies have shown that it strongly stimulates the female to approach the male.

How does man fit into this picture? We know from a steadily increasing body of fossil evidence that our species has in fairly recent geological times evolved from ape-like animal forms. However unique our species seems at first glance, this uniqueness must rest on differences of degree: our apparently "novel" characteristics must have evolved from animal roots. And though we are still far from understanding how our typically human traits have evolved, we begin to recognize, however dimly, possible precursors of human behaviour in animals. Man may seem unique in his ability to learn—but many animals learn extremely well, and animal studies are even giving us new ideas about improved teaching methods. Man's capacity for looking into the future, for assessing the probable future effects of his actions, is much more highly developed than that of any animal, but as we have seen, animals do show primitive forms of stimulus expectation. Our powers of abstraction, concept formation and cause-effect understanding may well be proliferations of abilities we see in animals. Social animals have crude precursors even of some of our "moral" standards, such as the primitive altruism of animal parents, inhibitions of aggression through "appeasement" behaviour, respect for a leader. Our poor understanding of these things is due to the fact that so far we have hardly applied the same methods of study to ourselves that we are applying to animals—it is astonishing but true that we do not even have a good *descriptive* knowledge of the most common behaviour patterns of human infants, let alone adults.

The evolution of human society and behaviour in the last 10,000 years or so has proceeded much more rapidly than in any other animal. It is good to remember, however, that most if not all of this evolution is due to a different process from that which I have been discussing. There is little indication that we have changed much genetically since Cro-Magnon man first appeared; most of our change is the product of handing on learned knowledge. Even this "psycho-evolution", as Julian Huxley has called it, is not something fundamentally new. New habits spread in a similar way in animal populations too; it is merely the scale which is different. But psycho-evolution has had one uniquely dangerous consequence: we have changed our environment, including our social environment, so fast that it has outpaced our genetically determined behavioural adaptation. We cannot possibly hope to speed up our genetic evolution sufficiently to cope with these often terrifying changes. Our only hope lies in adjusting ourselves by learning to cope with our new environment. This is why the study of man's behaviour, though emphatically not "the only proper study of mankind", is, equally emphatically, a task of the greatest urgency.

TUCKING PAPER STRIPS INTO THEIR RUMP FEATHERS, FEMALE LOVE-BIRDS FOLLOW AN INHERITED TRAIT FOR CARRYING NESTING MATERIALS

Has Behaviour Evolved?

It most certainly has. Specialized behaviour has evolved among animals as the pressures of their environment have changed them physically. This is almost impossible to prove since we cannot see fossils "behave". But in animals today, we see the combination of structural adaptation and refined behavioural patterns, developed through many generations, that enables every species to survive.

A LOUISIANA HERON holds a fish it has just speared. Its principal hunting technique is to dance and pirouette about in shallow water, stirring up fish so that it can see and catch them.

A COMMON EGRET makes a swift jab at a passing needle-fish. Egrets usually hunt by stepping slowly and cautiously, freezing when they see a fish and catching it when within reach.

For Each, a Way to Fish

An excellent example of the way slight behavioural differences can enable similar species to make a living from the same environment is provided by some of the long-necked waders and swimmers that inhabit the southern coastal marshes of the United States. All share the same general habitat, all eat the same things, but each goes about its business in a slightly different fashion, with the result that they can all live together, each in its own niche, without getting in one another's way. The behavioural patterns that make this sharing possible have been worked out by natural selection over a long period. They are now set in the various species as surely as long necks and long bills.

FLIPPING ITS CATCH, the anhinga gulps down the fish head first. It never swallows a fish tail first; going down that way, the scales and fins would catch in its throat.

A DIFFERENT EGRET HABIT is this one of skimming low over the water on the wing, looking for any fish swimming just below the surface and picking them up with its bill as it flies.

AN ANHINGA is a diver. As it floats, it spreads its wings, casting a shadow that cuts the sun's glare from its eyes and attracts fish to the shade. Then the anhinga dives to catch them.

SEEMINGLY CHAOTIC, a community of black-headed gulls is actually a well-organized society. Crowding together of nests provides mutual aid against predators such as crows (7, key at right), isolated nests being liable to raids (1). On the other hand, crowding cannot be carried too far, and proper spacing out is ensured by the males, which staunchly defend their territories against their neighbours. Protective coloration helps to conceal the eggs and chicks from prowling foxes, whose tracks may be seen in the sand (13). After hatching, however, the white insides of the egg-shell fragments often serve to attract predators; a crow, spying a broken shell, knows where to

find a helpless chick (1). Neighbouring gulls may also eat the young and eggs, so while the male warns them off (2), the female hides a conspicuous shell fragment.

Living in mixed flocks all the winter, these gulls begin their mating rituals in early spring, when their white face feathers turn dark, providing them with stern masks for challenging each other during threatening displays. The territorial feeling of males rises now and sometimes two of them actually fight (10). More often, however, the battle does not go beyond fierce posturing. They may spread their wings and bob in an angry "choking" attitude (5) or they may emit their warning

"long calls", either at males on the ground (6) or in the air (3). These long calls not only frighten away trespassers but also attract unmated females. At this point the relations between a male and a female are a confused mixture. Still hostile and suspicious of one another, they adopt the head-down threatening attitude of two males (11) but reduce the threat a bit by standing parallel (12) and tilting their bills up, a friendly overture. Courtship progresses as both partners avert their threatening face masks (9). After several encounters the male regurgitates food for the female to eat (8), then lures her to the nesting site he has chosen by bobbing his head over it (4).

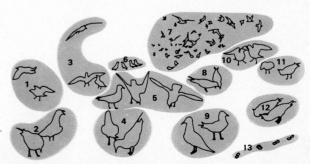

To Survive: Blend and Bluff

Certain animals, like the screech-owl and sphinx-moth shown on these pages, have developed behavioural traits that provide each with two distinct lines of defence against predators. Both these species are nocturnal and rely primarily on camouflage to protect them while resting during the day. Their habit of remaining motionless augments their highly evolved protective coloration. Should a predator see through the cryptic coloration, however, and threaten even further, the screech-owl (*below*) bluffs grandly, swelling, snapping and flapping. But the

A SCREECH-OWL when frightened first tries to blend even more into its surroundings by stretching itself tall and thin, and holding in all its feathers (*right*). But if this fails, it will pop its eyes, snap its bill and fluff out its feathers (*below*), making itself appear as fearsome as it can.

sphinx-moth (*below*) has a more subtle second line of defence. It flicks open its wings to expose eye-like spots, which often startle attackers, allowing the moth to escape. This simple act is a forceful example of behaviour developing in step with the evolution of body markings. Extensive studies by A. D. Blest have shown that moth species without eye-spots, when touched or otherwise disturbed, do not react by moving their wings in the same way as moths with eye-spots. Other moths that rely solely on camouflage for protection remain immobile even when poked.

A SPHINX-MOTH rests beneath its cryptically coloured forewings (*left*). When touched, the forewings jerk open, revealing bright spots on the hind wings (*below*). Surprised bird predators often drop the moth, mistaking these spots for the eyes of one of the animals that preys upon birds.

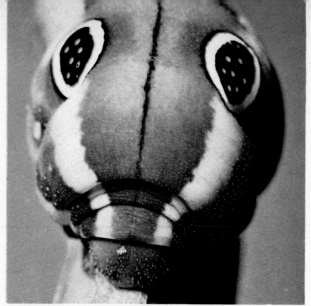

DISPLAYING ITS "HEAD" to a predator, the eye-spots of a hornworm expand as increased blood pressure swells the forward part of its body. The real head is scarcely visible in front.

Using Eyes for Defence

Caterpillars, on which eye-spots have evolved as part of their defence, have also developed behavioural displays that show their markings to best advantage. When endangered, many of these caterpillars bend or expand their bodies to form an outsized "head". Some species even rear up and sway, their false eyes made still larger as they puff up in specialized behaviour believed by most naturalists to be mimicry of snakes. Many larvae have eye-spots concealed in the folds of their skin and only reveal them when threatened. Some others have them underneath and display them by turning their bodies.

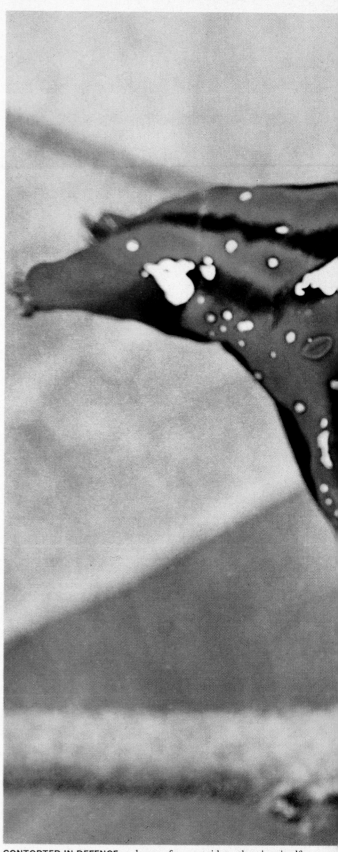

THE "EYE" ON THE REAR of an Abbott's sphinx larva is actually a vestigial horn. This caterpillar depends on the mark to shock a threatening bird out of its regular feeding pattern.

CONTORTED IN DEFENCE, a larva of a noctuid moth raises itself to scare off a predator. In this display, its real head is lowered and tucked in against the body, the two eye-like spots on each

side of the abdomen appearing prominently at the top of what appears to be the head when the body is folded. Lashing its body to and fro, this larva manages to compensate for its utter vulnerability by bluffing. The eye markings are also graphic evidence of the use of supernormal stimuli in defence; four false eyes are more frightening to a predator than two.

REMAINING MOTIONLESS, a tropical katydid clings to a branch and with luck will escape the sharp eyes of lizards, birds and monkeys that scour the trees in search of insect prey. Its wings are exactly like green leaves, even to the veins and blemishes, but the effect of these detailed structural refinements will be lost unless the katydid retains its adaptive stillness.

HUDDLED ON A LEAF, a tiny tropical frog has marks resembling a bird dropping, a protective coloration that demands complete stillness. Like the katydid and caterpillar seen on these pages, this frog is active at night, therefore its survival depends on its habit of resting without stirring for long hours during the daylight, its legs tucked inconspicuously underneath it.

Pretending to Be Inedible

Many animals gain protection by imitating, both in physical structure and behaviour, objects regarded as inedible by predators. A twig caterpillar (*right*), for example, has evolved the physical dimensions and markings of a real twig, but unless it remains as still as part of the tree, a predator will not be fooled and the insect will be eaten. Similarly, the creature must have the inclination to choose a suitable background in which to act like a twig. Thus, the background itself will influence the kind of behaviour that the animal uses. Nandid fish in the Amazon basin, for instance, resemble dead leaves and can float motionless among them for hours. Also, certain drab-coloured butterflies in America's tropics fly in such a way as to act like falling leaves, while some grasshoppers resemble fresh grass, others dried grass, and still others the stubble of burnt grass.

HOLDING A RIGID POSE, a twig caterpillar branches off a limb in the same manner as a real twig. If touched, this creature will fall to the ground, remaining motionless like a dead twig.

The Instinct to Hoard

In a study of the evolution of behaviour, the act of storing surplus foods by animals emerges as a specialized trait that aids the chances for survival. Insects like the harvester ants (*below*) are renowned for their overriding instinct for hiding food, but a wide range of creatures also has this compulsion to hoard. The nutcracker bird of Sweden stacks hazelnuts for winter use, draping them with lichens and remembering the locations of more than 85 per cent of these piles even when they are covered with deep snow. Carnivores of all sizes keep extra rations beyond the reach of competitors by storing. Weasels often cache small game prey, and giant grizzlies guard their hidden food reserves jealously. A mountain lion buries its kill, and may come back to eat and then re-bury the carcass as many as 10 times.

STORING GRAIN in one of the hundred or so chambers of the nest, harvester ants respond to their instinct to cache and care for food. Although the storage chambers are cool and dry, the seeds frequently become damp and germinate. The ants will then take them outside to dry in the sun or throw them away, or even seal up the oversprouted seeds in the storage chamber.

SPRAWLED ABOVE ITS KILL, a leopard rests on a branch after carrying a Thomson's gazelle into a tree where scavenging hyenas and jackals cannot reach it. The leopard will feed often from this carcass, regardless of its state of decay, until the entire animal is consumed. But if the leopard suspects another animal has eaten from the remains, it will not touch it again.

Bibliography

General

Bliss, Eugene L., ed., *The Roots of Behavior*. Harper, 1962.

Broadhurst, P. L., *The Science of Animal Behavior*. Pelican Books, 1963.

Cronwright-Schreiner, S. C., *The Migratory Springbucks*. Fisher Unwin, 1925.

Dethier, V. G., and Stellar, E., *Animal Behavior*. Prentice-Hall, 1964.

*Fabre, Jean Henri, *The Insect World of J. Henri Fabre*, ed. by Edwin Way Teale. W. S. Hall, 1949.

Goodwin, D., *Instructions to Young Ornithologists* (Vol. II): *Bird Behaviour*. Museum Press, 1961.

Hebb, Donald, *The Organization of Behavior*. Wiley, 1949.

Hediger, H., *Wild Animals in Captivity*. Academic Press, 1950

*Heinroth, Oskar and Katharina, *The Birds*. University of Michigan Press/Angus, 1958.

Jennings, H. S., *Behavior of the Lower Organisms*. Indiana University Press/W. S. Hall, 1962.

*Lack, David, *The Life of the Robin* (rev. ed.). Witheroy, 1947.

*Lorenz, Konrad, *King Solomon's Ring*. Crowell, 1961

*Maier, N.R.F., and Schneirla, T. C., *Principles of Animal Psychology*. McGraw-Hill, 1935.

Morgan, Conwy Lloyd, *Animal Behaviour*. Longmans, 1908.

*Scott, John P., *Animal Behavior*. University of Chicago Press, 1963.

Skinner, B. F., *The Behavior of Organisms*. Bailey, 1938. *Science and Human Behavior*. Collier-Macmillan, 1953.

Slater, Lloyd, ed., *Bio-Telemetry Symposium*. Pergamon, 1963.

Stevens, Stanley S., ed., *Handbook of Experimental Psychology*. Wiley, 1951.

Stevenson-Hamilton, J., *Wild Life in South Africa* (4th ed.). Cassell, 1954.

The Living Bird. Annuals of the Cornell Laboratory of Ornithology: No. 1, 1962; No. 2, 1963; No. 3, 1964 (all New York).

Thorpe, W. H., and Zangwill, O. L., eds., *Current Problems in Animal Behaviour*. Cambridge University Press, 1961.

Tinbergen, Niko, *Curious Naturalists*. Basic Books, 1959. *The Study of Instinct*. Oxford University Press, 1951.

Warden, Carl J., Jenkins, Thomas N., and Warner, Lucian H., *Comparative Psychology* (3 vols.). Wheldon & Wesley, 1935.

Evolution of Behaviour and Human Behaviour

Cain, A. J., *Animal Species and Their Evolution*. Harper, 1960.

Cott, H. B., *Adaptive Coloration in Animals*. Humanities Press, New York, 1964.

*Darwin, Charles, *The Diary of the Voyage of H.M.S. Beagle*. Cambridge University Press, 1962. *The Origin of Species and the Descent of Man*. Modern Library Giants, New York, 1936.

Fuller, J. L., and Thompson, W. R., *Behavior Genetics*. Wiley, 1960.

Grant, Verne, *The Origin of Adaptations*. Columbia University Press, 1963.

*Huxley, J. S., *Evolution—the Modern Synthesis* (2nd ed.). Harper, 1964. *Evolution in Action*. Harper, 1957.

Mayr, E., *Animal Species and Evolution*. Harvard University Press/O.U.P., 1963.

Roe, Anne, and Simpson, George Gaylord, eds., *Behavior and Evolution*. Yale University Press, 1958.

Russell, Claire and W.M.S., *Human Behaviour*. W. S. Hall, 1961.

Schiller, Claire H., ed., *Instinctive Behavior: The Development of a Modern Concept*. Bailey, 1964.

Symposia of the Zoological Society of London, No. 8, *Evolutionary Aspects of Animal Communication: Imprinting and Early Learning*. 1962.

Tax, Sol, ed., *Evolution after Darwin* (Darwin Centennial, 3 vols.). University of Chicago Press, 1960.

*Teilhard de Chardin, Pierre, *The Phenomenon of Man*. Harper, 1961.

Physiology of Behaviour

Beach, F. A., *Hormones and Behavior*. Harper, 1948.

Brown, Margaret, ed., *The Physiology of Fishes*: Vol. I—*Metabolism*; Vol. II—*Behaviour*. Academic Press, 1957.

Eccles, John Carew, *The Physiology of Nerve Cells*. Johns Hopkins Press/O.U.P., 1957.

Harlow, Harry F., and Woolsey, Clinton N., eds., *Biological and Biochemical Bases of Behavior*. University of Wisconsin Press/W. S. Hall, 1958.

Pringle, J.W.S., *Insect Flight*. Cambridge University Press, 1957.

Rockstein, Morris, ed., *The Physiology of Insecta* (3 vols. in prep.). Academic Press.

Roeder, Kenneth D., *Insect Physiology*, Wiley, 1953. *Nerve Cells and Insect Behavior*, Harvard University Press/O.U.P., 1963.

*Sherrington, Charles S., *The Integrative Action of the Nervous System* (2nd ed.). Cambridge University Press, 1947.

Symposia of the Society for Experimental Biology, No. 4, *Physiological Mechanisms in Animal Behaviour*. Cambridge University Press, 1950.

Wells, M. J., *Brain and Behaviour in Cephalopods*. Stanford University Press/O.U.P., 1962

Development and Learning

Foss, B., ed., *Determinants of Infant Behaviour*. Wiley, 1959.

Hediger, Heini, *Studies of the Psychology and Behaviour of Captive Animals in Zoos and Circuses*. Criterion Books, New York, 1956.

Rheingold, H. L., ed., *Maternal Behavior in Mammals*. Wiley, 1963.

Thorpe, W. H., *Bird Song*. Cambridge University Press, 1961. *Learning and Instinct in Animals* (2nd rev. ed.). Methuen, 1963.

Social Behaviour

*Allee, Warder C., *The Social Life of Animals*. W. S. Hall, 1938.

Armstrong, E. A., *A Study of Bird Song*. Oxford University Press, 1963.

Bastin, Harold, *Freaks and Marvels of Insect Life*. A. A. Wyn Inc., New York, 1954.

Butler, Colin G., *The World of the Honey Bee*. Collier-Macmillan, 1954.

Darwin, Charles, *The Expression of the Emotions in Man and Animals* (rev. ed.). W. S. Hall, 1955.

Etkin, W., ed., *Social Behavior and Organization Among Vertebrates*. University of Chicago Press, 1964.

Evans, Howard E., *Wasp Farm*. Doubleday Natural History Press, 1963.

Fabre, J. Henri, *Social Life in the Insect World*. The Century Company, New York, 1913.

Howard, Henry E., *Territory in Bird Life*. W. S. Hall, 1921.

Lanyon, W. E., and Tavolga, W. N., eds., *Animal Sounds and Communication*. American Institute of Biological Sciences, Publication No. 7, New York, 1960.

Lindauer, M., *Communication Among Social Bees*. Harvard University Press/O.U.P., 1961.

Meeuse, B.J.D., *The Story of Pollination*. Wheldon & Wesley, 1961.

Scott, John Paul, *Aggression*. University of Chicago Press, 1958.

Tinbergen, Nikolaas, *Social Behaviour in Animals*. Wiley, 1953.

Welty, Joel Carl, *The Life of Birds*. Knopf, 1963.

Wheeler, William Morton, *The Social Insects; Their Origin and Evolution*. Harcourt, Brace, 1928.

Sense Organs and Orientation

*Buddenbrock, Wolfgang von, *Senses*. University of Michigan Press/Cresset, 1958.

Carthy, J. D., *Animal Navigation* (2nd ed.). Scribner, 1957. *An Introduction to the Behaviour of Invertebrates* (2nd ed.). Allen & Unwin, 1962.

Dethier, V. G., *The Physiology of Insect Senses*. Wiley, 1963

Dorst, J., *The Migration of Birds*. W. S. Hall, 1962.

*Fraenkel, Gottfried S., and Gunn, Donald L., *The Orientation of Animals*. Dover, 1961.

Frisch, K. von, *Bees: Their Vision, Chemical Senses and Language*. Cornell University Press, 1950. *The Dancing Bees*. Harcourt, Brace, 1961.

Griffin, Donald R., *Listening in the Dark*. Yale University Press, 1958.

Kellogg, Winthrop N., *Porpoises and Sonar*. University of Chicago Press, 1963.

Le Grand, Yves, *Light, Color and Vision*. Dover, 1957.

Matthews, G.V.T., *Bird Navigation*. Cambridge University Press, 1955.

Matthews, L. Harrison, and Knight, Maxwell, *The Senses of Animals*. London Museum Press, 1963.

Polyak, Stephen, *The Vertebrate Visual System*, ed. by Heinrich Klüver. University of Chicago Press, 1958.

Symposia of the Society for Experimental Biology, No. 16, *Biological Receptor Mechanisms*. Cambridge University Press, 1962.

Tinbergen, Niko, *The Herring Gull's World* (rev. ed.). Basic Books, 1961.

Williams, C. B., *Insect Migration*. Collier-Macmillan, 1958.

* Available also in paperback.

Credits

The sources for the illustrations in this book are shown below.
Credits for pictures from left to right are separated by commas, top to bottom by dashes.

Cover—Treat Davidson from The National Audubon Society
8—Andreas Feininger
10, 11—drawings by Joseph Cellini
14—drawings by Lois and Louis Darling
17 to 33—Nina Leen
34—Hermann Eisenbeiss from Photo Researchers, Inc.
37—drawings by Lois and Louis Darling
39—drawings by Lois and Louis Darling
40—drawing by Lois and Louis Darling—drawings by Elmer Smith
41—drawings by Elmer Smith
42, 43—drawings by Lois and Louis Darling
45—Andreas Feininger
46—N. E. Beck from The National Audubon Society—Westinghouse Electric Corporation
47—Westinghouse Electric Corporation
48—Karl Daumer except bottom Ernest L. Libby
49—Fritz Goro
50—courtesy Columbia University Zoological Library, courtesy Department of Entomology, Oxford
51—Roman Vishniac
52 to 59—paintings by George V. Kelvin
60—Ralph Morse
62 to 68—drawings by Lois and

Louis Darling
69—Louis Darling
70 to 73—paintings by Lowell Hess
74—top Eric V. Gravé; bottom Lincoln P. Brower
75—top Eric V. Gravé; bottom Philip S. Callahan
76, 77—Pierre Boulat
78, 79—Thomas D. McAvoy
80—Tokutaro Tanaka
81—Eric Hosking
82—Keystone—Paul Lemmons from Frank W. Lane
83—George Silk
84—Tokutaro Tanaka picture for Orion from PIP photos
89, 90, 91—drawings by Lois and Louis Darling
93—Nina Leen
94, 95—diagram by Isador Seltzer
96—Aldo Margiocco
97—Walter Leuthold
98, 99—Akhtar Hussein
100, 101—Hermann Kacher
102—U.S. Army
103—Arthur Leipzig
104—Peter N. Witt except top left Eric Schaal; centre right Dieter Wolff, Zeitschrift Fuer Vergleichende Physiologie Volume 33 Springer Verlag, Heidelberg, 1951
105—Peter N. Witt
106—Bernard Hoffman
108 to 111—drawings by Lois and

Louis Darling
114—drawings by Lois and Louis Darling
115—Hermann Kacher
116, 117—Frederic A. Webster
118, 119—John Zimmerman
120—G. Edgar Folk—Marshall Lockman from Black Star, James Drake
121—© 1964 National Geographic Society Photo by Frank and John Craighead
122—C. G. Hampson from Annan Photo Features
123—I. Eibl-Eibesfeldt—Douglas P. Wilson
124, 125—John Dominis
126—William Vandivert
130, 131—drawings by Lois and Louis Darling
133—drawings by Lois and Louis Darling prepared by permission from an illustration © 1959 by Scientific American, Inc. All rights reserved
134—drawings by Lois and Louis Darling from *Bird-Song* by W. H. Thorpe; Cambridge University Press
137, 138—Lilo Hess
139—left Wallace Kirkland; right Eckhard H. Hess
140, 141—Robert W. Kelley
142—Frank L. Miller from Black Star
143—Ben Mancuso, Impact Photos, Inc.

144, 145—I. Eibl-Eibesfeldt
146, 147—Lee Boltin with Jane and Lincoln P. Brower
148, 149—PIP photos
150—Jean Prévost
152 to 156—drawings by Lois and Louis Darling
159—Niko Tinbergen
160, 161—drawings by Rudolf Freund
162—drawings by Hermann Kacher
163—paintings by Hermann Kacher
164, 165—Carleton Ray from New York Zoological Society
166—Shelly Grossman
167—I. Eibl-Eibesfeldt courtesy J. Nicolai
168, 169—David Goodnow for Sports Illustrated
170—Edward S. Ross
173 to 177—drawings by Lois and Louis Darling
179—William Vandivert
180, 181—Shelly Grossman
182, 183—Painting by Guy Tudor
184—Shelly Grossman
185—Alexander B. Klots
186, 187—Edward S. Ross except bottom left Alexander B. Klots
188, 189—Edward S. Ross
190—Aldo Margiocco
191—B. Grzimek from Tierbilder Okapia
Back Cover—Matt Greene

Acknowledgments

The editors of this book are particularly indebted to Daniel S. Lehrman, Professor of Psychology and Director, Institute of Animal Behavior, Rutgers University, and Kenneth D. Roeder, Professor of Physiology, Tufts University, who read the book in its entirety. They also want to thank: Dean Amadon, Curator of Ornithology, The American Museum of Natural History; Fred Aronson; James Atz, Bingham Oceanographic Laboratory, Yale University; William Baum; Lincoln P. Brower, Associate Professor of Biology, Amherst College; Helmut K. Buechner, Professor of Zoology, Washington State University; Philip S. Callahan, entomologist, U.S. Department of Agriculture, Entomology Research Division; Eugenie Clark, Executive Director, Cape Haze Marine Laboratory; Frank C. Craighead Jr., Research Associate, Wildlife Research Unit, Montana State University; Jocelyn Crane, Director of Department of Tropical Research, New York Zoological Society; I. Eibl-Eibesfeldt, Max Planck Institute for Comparative Behavior; G. Edgar Folk, Arctic Aerodynamical Laboratory, Fairbanks, Alaska; S. Frenk, University of Chile; Karl von Frisch; Murray Glusman, Senior Research Psychiatrist, New York State Psychiatric Institute; Harold J. Grant Jr., Chairman, Department of Insects, Academy of Natural Sciences of Philadelphia; Donald Griffin, Chairman, Department of Biolo-

gy, Harvard University; Harry F. Harlow, Director, Primate Laboratory, University of Wisconsin; Eckhard H. Hess, The Animal Behavior Laboratory, University of Chicago; Robert A. Hinde, Professor of Zoology, Sub-Department of Animal Behaviour, Cambridge University; Hermann Kacher, Max Planck Institute for Comparative Behavior; Dennis Kelly, Research Assistant, New York State Psychiatric Institute; John A. King, Associate Professor of Zoology, Michigan State University; Konrad Z. Lorenz, Director, Max Planck Institute for Comparative Behavior; Humberto R. Maturana, University of Chile; B.J.D. Meeuse, Professor of Botany, University of Washington; Andrew J. Meyerriecks, Professor of Zoology, University of South Florida; J. Nicolai, Max Planck Institute for Comparative Behavior; Roger Tory Peterson; Edward S. Ross, Curator of Entomology, California Academy of Sciences; Wolfgang Schleidt, Duke University; Dietrich Schneider, Max Planck Institute for Comparative Behavior; Theodore C. Schneirla, Curator, Department of Animal Behavior, The American Museum of Natural History; B. Frederick Skinner, Professor of Psychology, Harvard University; John Williams, Ornithologist, Croyden Museum; Ann Young, Research Associate, Department of Animal Behavior, The American Museum of Natural History.

Index

Numerals in italics indicate a photograph or painting of the subject mentioned.

✗✗✗✗✗

Typesetting by C. E. Dawkins (Typesetters) Ltd., London,
Smeets Lithographers, Weert, Printed in Holland
Bound by Proost and Brandt N.V., Amsterdam